David Cowger

Golf

FIT FOR GOLF
FIT FOR LIFE

FIT FOR GOLF
FIT FOR LIFE

THE ULTIMATE GOLF FITNESS AND FLEXIBILITY GUIDE

RANDY MYERS

DIRECTOR OF FITNESS FOR THE
2016 U.S. RYDER CUP TEAM

CLASSICS
OF GOLF

The world's best reading golf books.

CLASSICS OF GOLF

The world's best reading golf books.

Classics of Golf
50 Gedney Street
Nyack, New York 10960
classicsofgolf.com
845-765-6050

First Classics of Golf printing, 2017

ISBN No. 978-0-940889-75-0

Library of Congress Cataloging-in-Publication Data is available

For contact or ordering information write:
info@classicsofgolf.com

Manufactured in the United States of America

10 9 8 7 6 5 4 3 2 1

CREDITS
Principal photography: Eliot VanOtteren
Montana Pritchard/PGA of America: 16
Marc Player: 119

Find these and other Classics of Golf books at classicsofgolf.com:

A.W. Tillinghast: Creator of Golf Courses
by Philip Young

The Anatomy of Greatness: Lessons from the best golf swings in history
by Brandel Chamblee

The Life and Times of Donald Ross
by Chris Buie

Erin Hills: Host of the 2017 U.S. Open Championship
Photography by Paul Hundley, Written by Gary D'Amato

Unfriended: Power Brokers, Political Correctness & Hypocrisy In Golf
by Ted Bishop, 38th President of the PGA

TABLE OF CONTENTS

I'D JUST ARRIVED BACK HOME ON ST. SIMONS ISLAND, GA., after missing the cut at the 2015 PGA Championship and the text messages were already piling up from Randy Myers.

"Okay, Love Man. Monday morning, be ready to go."

He also wanted me to train on Tuesday morning, before I headed to Greensboro, N.C., for my next event, the Wyndham Championship. It was standard Randy, always pushing, always on point, always positive.

The 2015 season hadn't been my best. I'd had surgery on my right foot in April that kept me from playing for two months and at 51 years old competing against younger, stronger players was becoming more of a challenge.

Not that Randy cared much about my age or my tender right foot. In fact, he was waiting for me the day I had the surgery, perched on my weight bench in my garage when I arrived home with a workout/rehabilitation program already crafted. I was still under anesthesia—that's how committed he is. He knew I needed to have a good attitude. It wasn't about getting stronger. Randy's goal was to create a recovery program to keep me working and focused.

I'M NOT AS FIT AS TIGER WOODS OR RORY MCILROY, BUT I AM PREPARED TO PLAY THANKS TO RANDY AND THE PROGRAMS HE'S CREATED FOR ME OVER THE YEARS.

It was the same after I had neck surgery in 2013 and following multiple procedures on my left ankle in 2007 and '08. He always keeps me motivated and moving in the right direction, which he did again in Greensboro at the 2015 regular-season finale. We didn't work out that week, just stretched and talked, and eventually celebrated my 21st PGA Tour victory. It was a milestone that wouldn't have been possible without Randy.

When I injured my left ankle in 2007, my therapist told me that if I wouldn't have been working with Randy for the last year and a half, I probably wouldn't have recovered as quickly, or perhaps at all.

It's why when Bill Jones, the former chairman and CEO of Sea Island Resort, told me he wanted the best trainer in golf for the resort's Performance Center, Randy was an easy choice. It's why Randy was a key part of the United States team room at the 2016 Ryder Cup, organizing our fitness area and coordinating with each player's trainer to assure everyone was ready to play.

Growing up, my father and swing coach, Davis Love Jr., was like most players in his era who considered fitness to be detrimental to the golf swing. You didn't go near the gym if you wanted to play your best, but thanks to Randy and other trainers, fitness has evolved into a fundamental part of every top player's training.

I'm not as fit as Tiger Woods or Rory McIlroy, but I am prepared to play thanks to Randy and the programs he's created for me over the years.

We didn't start out lifting a bunch of weights and camp out in a gym. Instead, Randy focused on my flexibility and mobility that would allow me to play my best over a career that has now stretched to more than three decades.

A few years ago, some trainers in the Tour's fitness truck told me I wasn't the hardest worker, but I was the most consistent and that's because of the energy and insight that Randy has provided me. It doesn't take an hour and a half in the morning and an hour and a half in the afternoon in the gym to play your best golf, just 15 to 20 minutes of warm-up before each round, three to four workouts a week, and a little bit of motivation, which is Randy's specialty.

I learned a long time ago that with Randy, you get real positive real fast, and you get real results.

—Davis Love III

MEET RANDY MYERS

FOR THE LAST 12 YEARS, I've been the Director of Fitness at Sea Island Resort on the Georgia coast and its renowned Golf Performance Center where many of today's top Tour pros train. I work with many of them in the fitness center and more than 20 weeks a year on the road at tournaments, including Davis Love III, Billy Horschel, and Zach Johnson, among others.

But fitness assessments and regimens aren't just for top pros; they're for everyday golfers, too, and are a big part of our instruction program because the swing teachers at Sea Island need to know a player's physical limitations and abilities before they can really help the player improve. As the golf swing becomes more of a science, we've learned that physical limitations, more so than talent or even dedication, often make basic swing motions difficult or even impossible. It's not just grip, posture and setup anymore. It's how far can you turn? Do you have good range of motion? Are you able to rotate with speed? Do you finish in balance? We now know that a better body means better golf.

While the link between good balance and flexibility and a good golf swing is fairly common knowledge today, it wasn't always the case. In fact, it was just the opposite. When Brad Faxon first arrived on the PGA Tour in 1984, which, coincidentally, coincided with the first year of the fitness trailer, Chi Chi Rodriguez put an arm around him and pointed to the van.

"Son," he said in that wonderful accent of his, "I'm going to help you out right now. If you want to stay out on Tour, stay out of that gym."

Back then, no one could actually say if exercise and stretching helped golfers get any better. Many, like Chi Chi, thought it could hurt your game because you'd become too

Butch Harmon weighs in...

"The secret with amateurs is to get the most out of your ability. My dad used to say we can't make a racehorse out of a mule but we can damn sure make a racy mule. If you get your body in better shape that mule is going to run faster. One of the first stops for any student when they arrive at my golf school in Las Vegas is a physical assessment. It's the same TPI assessment that Randy helped design. It's amazing to me how many players are locked up in their hips. I know I have a problem with that. They just can't do the things we want them to do, where 10, 12 years ago you wouldn't even have known that.

"With Randy, whom I've worked with regularly for more than two decades to refine players like Dustin Johnson and Davis Love III, I've found a crucial component to my modern teaching model. I tell Randy what things he needs to watch out for and he is incredible at helping my players overcome their deficiencies. Everything he does is golf related. He's a trainer, he plays halfway decent, he understands the golf swing, he's worked with a lot of really successful players. Everything he's done is to get the individual, no matter who they are and what their problem is, in better shape to allow them to do the things they need to do in their golf swing. He understands that better than anybody."

bulky or injure yourself lifting weights and perhaps there was some truth to that. At the time, the little fitness that did apply to golf was limited to basic weight training that was largely borrowed from other sports with little or no regard for how the exercises would impact the golf swing, a multi-dimensional action that is based more on balance and flexibility than brute strength.

Fast forward five years later to 1989 when I was working on my Masters' degree at Penn State after graduating from West Chester University, where I was on the football team. I was also working as a graduate assistant strength coach for the Nittany Lions' football team and was looking for a topic for my graduate school thesis. Legendary football coach, Joe Paterno, agreed to sit with me and after an intense discussion, Mr. Paterno urged me to leave football, which has thousands of research papers and professionals. He advised me to direct my attention to something that I could own—something like golf.

This book has its roots in that 90-page thesis, "A Strength Training and Flexibility Program for Recreational Golfers"—the first detailed examination ever done on the impact of fitness in golf, as far as I know. Thank you, Mr. Paterno.

My research took me to south Florida, the unofficial East Coast home of retirement golf and the PGA of America, the 28,000-strong organization for club pros where, in 1992, I became the Director of Fitness.

Our research consisted of three groups of 50 participants each. For Group A, we tested their swing speed and that was it. Group B we put into a flexibility program two days a week, while Group C did strength training and stretching two days a week. At the end, Group A's swing speed didn't change, of course. B gained two miles per hour of club speed, which translates into 10 yards just by stretching. But C gained five miles per hour of swing speed, which was staggering. It's still one of the benchmark studies in golf.

Despite our results, it was difficult to get the word out about the benefits of a golf fitness program, but then one day that summer in walked the man who had been singing its praises for years, the irrepressible Gary Player. Then 57, the 5-foot-7-inch South African arrived at my windowless, 600-square-foot gym at PGA National Resort & Spa after having forged a Hall of Fame career by outworking his opponents both on the course and, some would say more importantly, in the gym. Here was a guy who was "The Man" when it came to being fit and he was interested in more. For a young trainer like me it was like, Wow, I can't believe he wants to keep learning. It is still one of the greatest thrills of my career.

We discussed exercise, diet and health, and how they specifically relate to golf. Gary wanted to win in his sixth decade and for all the mystique surrounding his fitness

Mike Bender weighs in...

"Randy was a pioneer. He's just got this incredible amount of energy and positive attitude. It's like what David Leadbetter did for teaching. Randy got involved early with the PGA and physical fitness and then Tiger Woods busted things wide open. It showed that you didn't have to be afraid of the gym.

"At my school, we have a preference with how we want players to swing, but you have to ask, is their body able to do that? That's why you need a trainer like Randy to understand how to get around the tendencies they have in their golf swing. You can teach around someone's body limitations but that's not ideal. I've worked with Zach Johnson since 1998 and couldn't believe the improvement in his game after he started working with Randy in the early 2000s. Now that dedication to training has trickled down to the amateur level in recent years, with players at all levels more willing to add a fitness component to their game. Just a few things can have a huge benefit with their swing."

regimen, he realized he needed to strengthen his lower body and improve his mobility. He had also lost flexibility and range of motion, like most players his age and, ultimately, wanted to hit the ball farther. But despite a lifetime dedicated to fitness and its impact on the golf swing, Gary wasn't convinced his gym routine was making him better on the golf course. That's when the light bulb went on for me. A lot of guys like to work out, but the golf specificity was really not predictable despite my study. People didn't know if it was truly helping their golf game.

One person who did was Dr. Gary Wiren, the PGA of America's director of education at the time who was Player's avant-garde counterpart in the teaching professional ranks. He had begun to incorporate more fitness elements into the association's teaching manual. About that same time at PGA National, we had more students coming through our golf schools than anyone else. The director of instruction, Mike Adams, averaged 100 schools a year with more than 30 students in each class and that's where my physical evaluations of golfers first began to take shape. It was an unreal learning experience because we discovered how quickly students could improve their swings with more range of motion.

I'm sure Jack doesn't realize this, but his commitment to golf continues to shape my career on a daily basis. In the mid 1990s, the Golden Bear Tour in south Florida brought some of the best young pros to town for a series of events. Luckily for me, Mr. Nicklaus asked me to physically evaluate the golfers and put them on a proper fitness routine. If it was good for Jack's Tour, it was important for the players. The average age of my students shifted toward younger Tour players and afforded me a chance to see how these young guns generates so much speed. Jack Nicklaus is a golf icon and his powerful swing and dedication to developing proper exercise was and is still a driving force for this generation of elite players.

The support I received from Gary and Mike was crucial, as was meeting Todd Anderson, who was the head pro at Old Marsh Golf Club in Palm Beach Gardens, Fla. We met at a dinner party in March 1993 and before long, of course, we started talking about how fitness relates to the golf swing. We talked about the movements his students couldn't physically do. No matter how good a teacher Anderson was—and he's one of the best—every student comes with his or her unique variety of physical limitations and no amount of swing theory can compensate for limited hip rotation or a lack of lower body stability. We were the first two to really combine fitness and golf instruction, taking it to another level. We understood how important it was to be able to evaluate a person's limitations and how you incorporate that into working as a team to get

Randy with Jack Nicklaus in 1996.

better, which we have continued at Sea Island for the last 14 years.

Another person who saw the benefit of fitness was none other than Jack Nicklaus. When he started his Golden Bear Tour in south Florida in 1996, he wanted players to have access to tools to improve the mental and physical aspects of their game, so sport psychologist Rick Jensen and I worked with many of the players. Never before had there been a mini-tour in one central location where guys could hit balls, train, and work on their minds and bodies during a 12-tournament schedule to help them get to that next level.

But it wasn't really until 1998 when everything fell into place. That's when I met Dr. Greg Rose, who was pounding the same golf-fitness drum in Maryland. We had teamed up for a sparsely attended seminar at PGA National. Afterward, we sat in the resort's bar and wrestled with two essential questions: What do people need to know? And where does fitness go from here? Both questions led back to the same answer—the teaching professional, who historically viewed any type of training program as a detriment to the golf swing. One thing was clear: PGA professionals needed to better understand what their students couldn't do because of their physical limitations—no sense in teaching a swing theory that can't work.

Todd Anderson weighs in...

"No matter how well-informed my training methods are, every student comes with their unique variety of physical limitations and no amount of swing theory can compensate for limited hip rotation or a lack of lower body stability. Randy and I were the first two to marry fitness and golf instruction when I was at Old Marsh and he was at PGA National. We understood how important it was to be able to evaluate a person's limitations and how you incorporate that into working as a team to get better."

About a year later, we got a call from Wally Uihlein, the CEO of Titleist, who wanted to start a fitness program at their facility in Oceanside, Calif. That's how the Titleist Performance Institute and our 18-point assessment originated. It was designed to give teachers and club professionals, not just trainers or medical experts, the tools to identify a player's physiological weaknesses. It was the first screening test that brought the integration of teaching and fitness to the masses and the one you'll do in Chapter Two of this book. We also realized we needed to create an educational entity to certify trainers and instructors. I'm proud to say there are now more than 10,000 TPI-certified pros who are helping amateurs around the world become more golf fit.

After helping to establish TPI, I went on to work with college teams and high-level players, which had always been my goal. Bob Wood, the former president of Nike Golf, came to me in the early 2000s and said he wanted to evaluate juniors and college players in a way other than just by tournament results. I've worked with all the Nike-sponsored college golf teams: Florida State, Alabama, Vanderbilt, Virginia, Ole Miss, Penn State, Georgia, and Clemson, among others. I was always looking for outliers. I can pretty much tell after my assessment whether a high school or college player can play professionally because the evaluations are very golf-specific motion patterns. Asymmetries and lack of mobility put a cap on the ability for a player to improve, but if he or she has the balance to complete the motion, a good range of motion, and can do both sides equally, there's no limitation in what a player can do in his or her golf swing. There are exceptions, such as if you're a talented putter or chipper or just mentally very tough; but if you have limitations at an early age, while you can make improvements, you will always be behind the player who has no limitations. Only 12 players have fully passed my assessment in my 20-year career and all of them are on Tour and every one of them has won, including Dustin Johnson, Brooks Koepka and Morgan Pressel. They can load their hips, complete their mid-spine turn, and can rotate in both directions equally. There's no compensation in the swing.

As the word got out, players began to gravitate to my program at PGA National, where my gym would expand to more than 30,000 square feet (with windows, no less!) before I left for Sea Island Resort, where Todd had taken over as the Director of Instruction, in 2005. While we work with many of the game's best players, we also work with amateurs of all levels. Although the scores, and certainly the motivations, between pros and amateurs vary wildly, the basic tenets of each workout remain largely the same, which is what inspired this book. It will help you regardless of your ability level. Your improvement in golf is based to a large degree on your functionality, but the great thing is my program doesn't require a lot of time or effort or a lot of equipment. The routines can be done a few at a time at home in your spare time. The biggest impediment to working out is just getting to the gym. With my plan you don't need a gym, just some basic equipment. This book can help you as much if not more than a top teacher like Todd or Butch Harmon can because your body first needs to move correctly before it can swing correctly.

For the last 20 years, I've been honing the assessment and routines from what I've learned working with more than 60 PGA Tour professionals, hundreds of club pros and college players, and thousands of amateurs of all ages—men and women. I helped Davis Love III, the 1997 PGA Championship winner and victorious captain of the 2016 U.S. Ryder Cup team at Hazeltine, win a PGA Tour event at 51 years old in 2015 and Brandt Snedeker overcome not one but two hip surgeries and win the FedEx Cup in 2013. Lucas Glover credited me with helping him win the 2009 U.S. Open at Bethpage. I've helped 40 to 80 year olds with handicaps from 1-20 who wanted to play better, hit it farther, and play longer. I've helped more than 500 high school players get Division I scholarships.

Now I'm going to help you. Everything I've learned from these experiences is in this book and will help you play better longer and get more enjoyment out of the game. Golf might be 90 percent mental, but the mental part will be a whole lot easier if you get your body symmetrical and functional so you can execute. It's so much easier to be mentally strong when your body is powerful and efficient and can do what you need it to.

CHAPTER ONE

TEAM BUILDING

WHAT YOU CAN LEARN FROM THE VICTORIOUS 2016 U.S. RYDER CUP TEAM

A S ONE OF THE PIONEERS OF GOLF FITNESS whose players have won more than 100 times over the last 20 years, I've been lucky enough to have a front-row seat at every major tournament during that span. But nothing tops the Ryder Cup, where I've proudly served five teams, including two as the Director of Fitness. The final day at Medinah in 2012 when we lost after being ahead by four points was THE worst day I ever had in my career. Everyone was so disappointed when we had every opportunity to win the cup back after two straight losses. We came so close, thinking we were going to win almost until the end. We went from euphoria to despair in the span of an hour. But four years later, the last day at Hazeltine was THE best day I've ever had in my career. In the intervening four years, I had the incredible fortune of routinely working with three FedEx Cup winners (Bill Haas, Brandt Snedeker, and Billy Horschel) and another major champion (Zach Johnson at The Open Championship), but that whole low-to-high experience at the Ryder Cup is something I'll never forget.

U. S. Team Captain Davis Love III and Randy Myers at the 41st Ryder Cup Match at Hazeltine National Golf Club in Chaska, Minn.

What does this have to do with golf fitness? A lot. Clearly, you want to be the best golfer you possibly can be or you wouldn't have bought this book, so I want to share a little bit of what went on behind the scenes at Hazeltine and show you how important physical preparation is to the on-course performance of the best players in the world. To maximize your potential, you want to emulate them as much as possible. I also want to get you as pumped up as possible to become functionally fit.

After another stinging loss to Europe at Gleneagles in 2014, the PGA of America, which runs the Ryder Cup here in the U.S., put together a task force comprised of 11 past captains, players, and PGA of America leaders to overhaul the entire Ryder Cup process—everything from qualifying and how captains are selected to deadlines for captain's picks. But the real upshot was that the players would be more in charge, which meant that they would be able to have their own people around them and keep to similar routines like they do any at PGA Tour event or major. That consistency and familiarity allowed them to perform at their highest level at Hazeltine and was a huge reason why we won.

For the very first time, we had 12 players completely invested in the process, so it was a very close-knit group of guys. When Davis said, "This is the best team ever assembled," what he meant was, this was the most cohesive group of guys. They all got along and wanted everyone else to do well. It was all about, "Hey, what's best for this team?"

I'll give you a good example. After Phil Mickelson was critical of Hal Sutton, the 2004 captain, about how important a captain is in preparing his team, Sutton wasn't happy about it and it created a minor media ruckus. Captain Love was sitting around a table in the Team Room with the vice-captains and radioed for Phil to come in.

"Okay, just give it to me now," Phil said with that sheepish grin of his. "I screwed up."

But instead of calling him out, Davis said, "You didn't screw up. What do you want us to do right now to take the pressure off of you?" Phil was just dumbfounded and said, "I've been in many of these things and no one has ever said, 'How can I help you?' That's an important thing to me. I got this."

It was all for one and one for all. The preparation aspect is even more important in a team game like the Ryder Cup because nobody wants to let his teammates down. Everyone's preparation is different, but let's use Zach as an example. He likes to get to the course two hours and 15 minutes before his tee time. He'll warmup anywhere between 30 and 45 minutes in the fitness trailer—basically doing the routine he demonstrates in Chapter Three—before getting stretched out. After a bite to eat, he'll put on his golf outfit, then warm-up with his clubs on the range. At Hazeltine, we built a training area in the locker room to simulate the fitness trailer on Tour, which, believe it or not, the Ryder

Fundamental golf specific warm-up movements are critical
for sustaining overall sports performance.

Cup players never had before! Other players simply get stretched, some get adjusted, some players just ride a bike and then stretch. But the point is, they're getting warmed up the way they feel they need to.

At Hazeltine, we had a True Stretch apparatus, as well as benches, weights, cable machines, bikes, bands, balls, whatever was needed. Each player also received one of my Stretching Poles (which you'll learn about in Chapter Thirteen) with a Ryder Cup logo on it. But a lot of it was about asking these guys, "What do you want, what do you need?" The No. 1 thing they wanted was access for their therapist to be there. In the past, the locker-room was like Fort Knox. The only people who had access were the captains, the players, and the player- and caddie-liaisons. There are still no agents or equipment manufacturers, but at Hazeltine their physio, chiropractor, and/or masseuse were allowed in. That was something in the past that the PGA of America fought tooth and nail, but this time they said, "If the players want it, let's give it to them." Perhaps that doesn't seem like that big a deal, but that comfort level is extremely important given the pressure the players are under to perform.

Before Hazeltine, I was the only trainer allowed in the locker room. Although I work with between 12 and 20 guys in a normal week, not all of the guys on the team are mine, so to have someone else wash and wax your car, so to speak, there's a little bit of anxiety. Some players are fine with it, like Dustin Johnson, whom I've worked

Dustin Johnson played amazing golf at the 2016 Ryder Cup after winning his first major earlier in the year at the U.S. Open Championship at Oakmont.

with many times in the past. But a guy like Jimmy Walker, whom I've never work with, wanted his own guy there, and so did J.B. Holmes and Jordan Spieth. Most of the work is done after their rounds and in the past with all the social functions, players couldn't get their work in, but by eliminating a lot of the social functions and adding a stretching and treatment room on the Team USA floor at the hotel, the players were able to come back from the course and work with their therapists into the night. It was a massive advantage for the players.

It just goes to show you how important a better body has become to better golf in this game. Finally, in 2016, we're in a position where the players get what they need from a physical-preparation standpoint. It would be like if someone broke their 7-iron and couldn't get it fixed. That would never happen.

The fitness room was the busiest room in the clubhouse, not only with all the training but just because of all the camaraderie and fun that went on there. Everyone was pretty excited about it because it was so tailored to their needs. You'd have Jordan on one table getting worked on by his chiro, while Patrick Reed was getting in a training session. Tiger Woods worked out intensely every day and was involved with a lot of the players and their workouts, like Dustin. Guys were slapping each other on the feet, smacking each other with towels, getting pumped up, getting ready to go to battle. Much like the training room or locker room at any sporting event, this was where the players can be alone and get their game faces on.

The Team Room at the hotel, which was in a ballroom off the lobby, was also a lot of fun. There was always someone in there. The players would come in every night, eat, sign memorabilia, talk. Michael Jordan was there, as was Bill Murray. Darius Rucker (lead singer of Hootie and the Blowfish) performed after dinner a couple of times. There was a karaoke machine, videos playing, and photos flashing on flat screens of prior Ryder Cup players or the day's matches. It was a great place for the guys just to relax. No one wanted to stay in their room. Guys would come down in their pajamas. Rickie Fowler showed up in a Superman costume one time and a Rocky the Flying Squirrel outfit another just to keep everyone loose. There was a lot of gift giving. It was like Christmas. Dustin Johnson, for instance, gave everyone a red, white, and blue eel-skin wallet with USA on it.

Before the start of play, everyone got up and spoke after dinner Thursday night, including Mike Eruzione, the captain of the 1980 Olympic hockey team. He recalled how his coach, Herb Brooks, said that you have one chance at greatness and if you don't give it your absolute all, you'll take it to your grave, so for the rest of the week we were like, "Don't take this to your grave!"

Phil spoke on numerous occasions and had these guys pumped up. He was definitely the team leader and was a big influence on the players. Best I've ever seen him. He talked a lot about his historical view and how the best teams he's been on were ones where the players played for the betterment of the team, not just for their own satisfaction. Sacrifice was important. Phil's big thing was, get your rest, get your preparation done but don't over prepare. Just be ready to play.

Tiger was also a rock and very involved, particularly with the pairings. He had a notebook filled with all kinds of plans, cold weather pairings versus hot weather, wet versus dry. Davis had assigned him to the pod that included Patrick, who reveres Tiger to the point of wearing black and red on Sunday. I don't think it's any coincidence that Patrick turned in one of the all-time great Ryder Cup performances with his idol mentoring him.

Davis had done a lot of research on why New England Patriots' coach Bill Belichick is so successful at developing players who weren't always the top draft picks, as well as taking the top picks and making them leaders. Davis took us to the Patriots' training camp the week of the PGA Tour stop in Boston in early September to meet him and

With Brandt Snedeker after the U.S. Ryder Cup victory.

Bill's number one thing was, "Do your job. Don't worry about anyone else or the hype, just do your job."

There was also a big push this time with better hydration and nutrition, which you'll read more about in Chapter Ten. At Medinah, we were just starting to experiment with it, but the Task Force made it a big point of emphasis for the players, having plant-based protein meals that can be mixed and be eaten multiple times a day. We took into consideration food allergies of any players, who had an order sheet to get whatever they wanted. The special proteins we used and recovery shakes were not only very popular, but they were a big advantage for us. Phil is really into nutrition because of his psoriatic arthritis, which includes about four cups of coffee a day because he finds it alleviates the pain. He uses a specific coffee blend and almond milk and other things, but that was one thing we provided for him. It certainly paid off. He made 10 birdies in his Sunday singles match.

It's hard to believe, but we never had a specific nutrition plan before at the Ryder Cup and it was a big part of our success. Frankly, when I saw what the Europeans were eating, those sandwiches in plastic containers that you get at the British Open, I thought, we got this one. There was no doubt we had an upper hand when it came to diet. In the past, guys would be too rushed to eat effectively, but this time every golf cart had a cooler packed with healthy snacks like almond butter sandwiches and Vega protein bars.

I'll say this about the Europeans: they were as dedicated in their workouts as we were. After we put ourselves in a good position on Friday evening with a 5–3 lead, I was working out in the hotel gym around 9:30 and saw half the European team there going through their workouts, including Rory McIlroy, Martin Kaymer, and Danny Willett. That was the first time I saw more of their players participating in a training session than ours. They might have been down, but they weren't out. The best players in the world always carry that eternal hope.

I have so many great memories from the week, like seeing Zach and Brandt, two guys I've worked with for years, get their first Ryder Cup win. That was an incredible feeling. But perhaps my fondest memory of the week came at the very end when Ryan Moore, the last guy to make the team, won the winning point. After he made it, Davis took the ball out of the hole because his ball went missing in 1993 when he clinched the victory. He handed it to Ryan and said, "I want you to have this. Someone took mine in '93. It's important." About 15 minutes later, Ryan came up to Davis and said, "I want you to have the ball. This is for you." That kind of a sums up the whole week.

This all relates back to the concepts for the book—prepare your body to perform its best by building a team. You need to have your own team: a putting instructor, a full-swing teacher, a mental coach, a club-fitter, and a fitness trainer, and maybe even a nutritionist. If you don't and you're in your club championship or just playing a $5 Nassau, you're going to get beat if the guy or gal you're going against has a team together. Even if you can't afford an actual team, build a virtual one by relying on instruction books like this one. You better be calculated with your whole routine and what you're doing and why; otherwise, you're just treading water when it comes to your performance, while others are swimming laps.

I hope I've gotten you a little bit excited about what's to come. Now let's get started making your body better so you can play better golf!

With Matt Ginella on Morning Drive on Golf Channel.

CHAPTER TWO

FLEXIBILITY ASSESSMENT

IDENTIFYING YOUR STRENGTHS AND PHYSICAL LIMITATIONS

S PEND ENOUGH TIME ON A PRACTICE RANGE and one thing quickly becomes obvious: everyone swings differently. Some of those distinctions are based on technique and swing style, while others are based on the way your body moves, or in some cases doesn't move.

Every golf swing, from the Tour player all the way down to the guy who is trying to break 100, is largely based on individual flexibility, and these limitations become more exaggerated as you age. Identifying those weaknesses is the initial element of any fitness program and why this assessment portion is crucial. In fact, it should be the first thing you do every day before you play. My Tour players do it and so should you because just doing the assessment routinely will improve your proficiency in that area.

The goal is to complete all 18 assessments at or above a Tour level, but most people won't have the ability to complete all of them successfully because of physical limitations from sitting at a desk all day or injuries that have led to restrictions and weaknesses in a particular area. The good news is you can recover much of what you lost with the help of this book. There are likely going to be individual assessments you struggle to complete and identifying these problem areas will help you fine-tune your fitness program for your swing and your body type.

DAVIS LOVE III has been a golf icon for over 25 years. His ball striking is legendary. Davis generates his speed with excellent fundamentals and exceptional balance. He is extremely fit and focuses on maintaining his flexibility and stamina.

It's important to focus on your form during each assessment with the goal of performing 8 to 10 repetitions of each when you start to incorporate them into your workout program. If you can only manage 3 to 5 repetitions at the start, that's okay. The key is that you start. It's also important to realize that if you struggle with a particular motion or area you'll need to spend more time focused on these problem areas.

You can change your flexibility, but you need to commit to the 2,000-rep rule, where it's going to take 2,000 reps to alter your body's movements. That might be as simple as 10 repetitions a day for six months, but you'll see improvements along the way. I also want you to remember that you're not training in a "bubble." The reason you started a fitness program is to improve your golf swing, and after going through two or three assessments take a moment to mimic a golf swing in a mirror. These "rehearsal swings" will allow you to gauge whether you've increased your range of motion by checking your backswing and follow through. You can do these with or without a golf club, but it's important to regularly check your progress throughout your entire assessment to keep your workouts as golf-centric as possible.

This is also where it's important to build your own team. Tour players have access to the best swing coaches, trainers and physical therapists, but that's probably not a realistic model for most golfers. Instead, you can use this book to improve and prepare your body for golf, and a PGA professional who understands your swing and what you hope to accomplish. If you want to be a great player you need a knowledgeable individual who knows your swing. It could be your son, your wife, or a PGA pro, but someone needs to be there to give you feedback on what you're doing well and what you need to work on.

Start every workout with this assessment so you will be able to identify areas of weakness as well as strengths. It will provide the same model that's used by the best players in the world and is easily scalable to every level of golfer to build a fitness plan that's structured to your specific needs. So grab a 7-iron and let's get started.

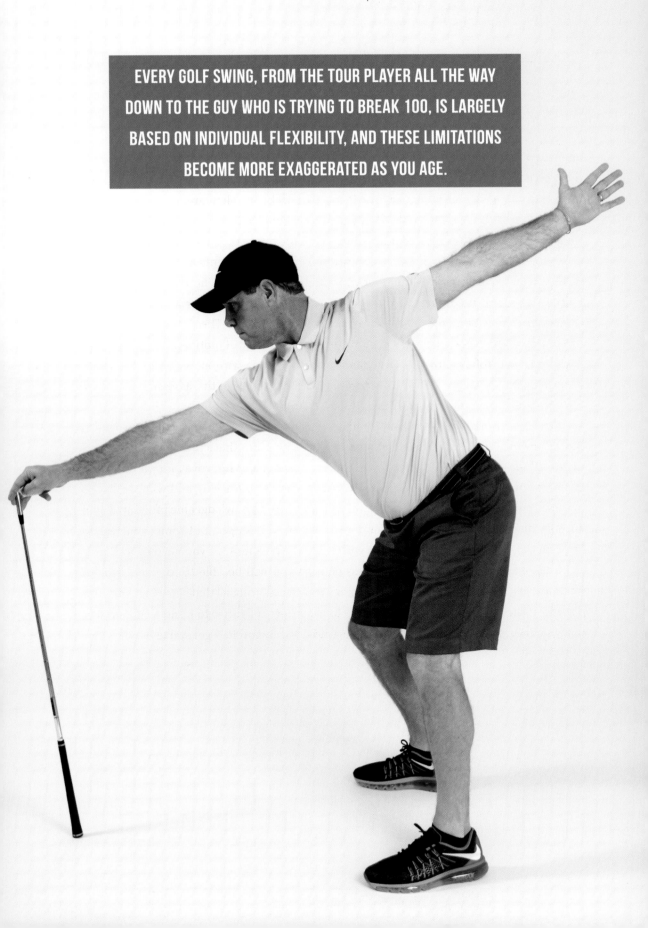

EVERY GOLF SWING, FROM THE TOUR PLAYER ALL THE WAY DOWN TO THE GUY WHO IS TRYING TO BREAK 100, IS LARGELY BASED ON INDIVIDUAL FLEXIBILITY, AND THESE LIMITATIONS BECOME MORE EXAGGERATED AS YOU AGE.

These initial six assessments will test the mobility and flexibility of your upper back and shoulders, which are crucial in making a full turn to get the most distance.

1. STRAIGHT-ARM PUSH

EVALUATION: With the butt of the grip on the ground, stack your hands atop the club head and bend at the waist, pushing your head down between your arms; keep your back flat and your hips back.

FAULT: Can't get your head below your arms.

FIX: Corrective No. 17 (Vertical-Elbow Lift) on page 49.

2. STRAIGHT-ARM PUSH/ONE-ARM LIFT

EVALUATION: From the same starting position as before, alternate lifting one arm vertically above you shoulder plane.

FAULT: Can't raise your arms straight above your head.

FIX: Corrective No. 9 (Low/High) on page 45.

3. VERTICAL PRESS

EVALUATION: From your golf posture hold the club over your shoulders, lift it vertically over your head, and try to drop it behind your neck. Be sure to keep your head forward and your back tilted but straight.

FAULT: Can't drop the club behind your neck.

FIX: Corrective No. 7 (Away from Body) on page 44.

4. ARMS-OVERHEAD HORIZONTAL REACH

EVALUATION: Hold the club over your head and attempt to maintain the same plane while you rotate to each side. Try to point the club at the ground.

FAULT: Can't get the club vertical and keep it on plane as you bend side-to-side.

FIX: Correctives No. 1 (Forward Flexion) and No. 5 (Arm Slide) on pages 41 and 43.

5. FORWARD LUNGE/VERTICAL-ARM LIFT

EVALUATION: Hold the club over your head, step forward in a lunge position, and lower the club in front of you before raising the club again; switch legs and repeat.

FAULT: Can't keep the club vertical in the lunge.

FIX: Corrective No. 8 (High/Low) on page 44.

6. ONE-LEG BALANCE STRAIGHT-ARM LIFT

EVALUATION: Hold the club knee high and stand on one leg.
Bend forward and extend your arms over your head; switch legs and repeat.

FAULT: Can't get your arms horizontal and/or lose balance.

FIX: Corrective No. 3 (Lateral Extension) on page 42.

The next six assessments will test the range and strength of your torso,
which is vital in maintaining the posture in your golf swing.

7. BEHIND-YOUR-BACK STRAIGHT-ARM LIFT

EVALUATION: Hold the club behind your backside with your palms facing forward,
bend forward, and try to lift your arms over your shoulders with your back horizontal
to the ground.

FAULT: Can't get your arms vertical.

FIX: Corrective No. 16 (Straight-Arm Lift) on page 48.

8. BEHIND-YOUR-BACK STRAIGHT-ARM LIFT/ROTATE

EVALUATION: From the same starting position as before, rotate side-to-side and try to point the club downward as much as possible.

FAULT: Can't keep your head centered and rotate the club toward the ground.

FIX: Corrective No. 18 (Torso Rotation) on page 49.

9. GOLF POSTURE/ALTERNATE-ARM REACH

EVALUATION: From your golf posture with the butt of the grip on the ground, hold the club head with one hand and reach back as far as you can with the opposite arm. Try to keep your arm on the same plane as your shoulders and limit your hip rotation; switch arms and repeat.

FAULT: Can't get your arm behind you and keep it on your shoulder plane.

FIX: Corrective No. 4 (Elbow Squeeze) on page 42.

10. STRAIGHT-ARM TORSO ROTATION

EVALUATION: Hold the club just outside your right pocket with your arms extended and try to turn toward the club as you bend at the waist. The goal is to be able to extend the left shoulder over the right knee; repeat on your left side.

FAULT: Can't make a full turn keeping both arms straight.

FIX: Corrective No. 15 (Open-Book Rotation) on page 48.

11. CLUB-ACROSS-CHEST TORSO ROTATION

EVALUATION: From your golf posture, hold the club horizontally across your chest and rotate right and left until the club is pointing at the ground. The goal is to be able to rotate the club until it's pointing to a spot close to the foot you're turning toward.

FAULT: Can't get the club pointed down.

FIX: Corrective No. 13 (Internal Hip Rotation) on page 47.

12. STRAIGHT-ARM LUNGE ROTATION

EVALUATION: From a lunge position, hold the club in front of you and rotate toward the forward leg. Keep your arms straight and the club horizontal to the ground; switch legs and repeat.

FAULT: Can't complete a full rotation and maintain balance.

FIX: Correctives No. 2 (Horizontal Rotation) and No. 6 (Across Body) on pages 41 and 43.

These final six assessments will test your range of motion and strength in your lower body—the key to generating power and consistency.

13. TOE TOUCH

EVALUATION: Hold the club horizontally in front of you and bend forward at the waist trying to touch your toes. You can bend your knees slightly to complete the exercise, but try to keep your back flat and feet square.

FAULT: Can't reach your toes without too much knee bend.

FIX: Corrective No. 19 (Toe Touch) on page 50.

14. HEEL TOUCH

EVALUATION: Hold the club behind your backside, bend at the waist, and slide the club as far down your calves as you can toward your heels with your legs straight.

FAULT: Can't keep reach your heels without bending your legs.

FIX: Corrective No. 20 (Upper-Body Rotation) on page 51.

15. ARMS-OUT SQUAT

EVALUATION: Stand up straight and hold the club straight out from your shoulders, then squat down while trying to keep your knees over your toes.

FAULT: Ankles roll in and/or heels come off the ground.

FIX: Corrective No. 10 (Knee Push) on page 45.

16. ARMS-OVERHEAD SQUAT

EVALUATION: Hold the club horizontally over your head and squat.
The goal is drop your hips below your knees while keeping the club over your head.
FAULT: Arms and body move forward too much and/or lose balance.
FIX: Corrective No. 12 (Figure-Four Stretch) on page 46.

17. ARMS-OUT SQUAT ROTATION

EVALUATION: Hold the club horizontally in front of you and squat down
with your arms and thighs parallel to the ground; rotate from side-to-side while
keeping your head in position.
FAULT: Limited rotation on either side.
FIX: Corrective No. 11 (Hip Extensions) on page 46.

18. CLUB-ACROSS-CHEST ONE-LEG ROTATION

EVALUATION: From your golf posture with the club folded horizontally across your chest, raise your left leg behind you, and turn your left shoulder over your right toe; hold it for three breaths then switch legs, holding your right shoulder over your left toe.

FAULT: Limited rotation and/or lose balance.

FIX: Corrective No. 14 (Cross-Leg Bridge) on page 47.

SUMMARY

Now that you've completed the evaluation, you should feel energized and ready to practice or play because your body has just woken up with golf-specific exercises. My Tour pros routinely perform these assessments in the fitness trailer before they ever hit a ball on the range in order to get their bodies to move consistently every day and see if they have any problem areas that they need to address. As you continue to do them over time, you'll be able to complete them more successfully, which, in turn, will allow you to swing the club more consistently. Even if you struggled with some of them, you're already on your way to a better body and better golf.

LUCAS GLOVER is an outstanding example of a big man who is exceptionally flexible. A former baseball player, Lucas smashes the ball off the tee with tremendous speed and accuracy. His gym work is consistent and regular, focusing on upper body strength and core work.

CHAPTER THREE

CORRECTIVES

INJURY RECOVERY AND PREVENTION

I F YOU DID NOTHING ELSE but the corrective moves in this chapter, that would be a big start to improving your range of motion and your golf swing. If you play golf long enough, you're almost certain to suffer some sort of injury along the way. The one-sided, repetitive nature of the game has a tendency of identifying the slightest weaknesses and turning them into chronic ailments.

Chronic injuries are a part of the aging process and are often compounded by traumatic ailments like broken bones or torn ligaments. Throw in the fact that golf is notorious for creating injuries and you've got a perfect recipe for a body that doesn't function like it should. While the assessment portion of any fitness program is the most crucial, for players with injuries or severe lack of flexibility due to years of not addressing issues, it will be the specific correctives that will form the basis of a workout routine.

Consider Davis Love III, who has endured almost as many injuries as he has victories on the PGA Tour, resulting in ankle, back and hip surgeries, and all manner of less pressing, but just as concerning, nagging ailments. Yet the two-time U.S. Ryder Cup captain is a testament to the benefits of a dedicated corrective program. Here's a guy who still won on Tour even after all the injuries because he's realized he can still play effective golf at a very high level as long as he's conditioned and his body is functional. The only way to do that is to be able to focus on specific areas where you might be injured or recovering from surgery.

Nearly every golfer has dealt with some level of injury, which is why you should make a corrective program part of your fitness plan. My Tour players will perform their correctives after a round or workout as part of a cool down and the same program should apply to recreational golfers as well.

These stretches are designed to be slower movements that focus on particular areas that are weak or tight. In golf, there are essentially six areas where injuries or problems occur—ankles, knees, hips, back, shoulders and wrists. For the purposes of this program, I have narrowed that list down to four primary groups: neck and upper back, shoulders, lower and mid-back, and hips. The amount and frequency of a player's corrective program will be based entirely on their assessment. If you struggled in the deep-squat assessment, for example, you likely have a hip issue and will need to focus on those correctives, which is why I cross-referenced each assessment with the corresponding corrective in the previous chapter.

It's also important to keep your larger goals in perspective when it comes to committing to your correctives. Hitting the golf ball farther and more consistently is probably why you're reading this book and one of the biggest issues I've seen over my two decades of working with golfers of all levels is poor posture, which often relates to back issues. Back issues are the speed killer in golf, impacting everything from your set up to your backswing to your follow through. Identifying these weaknesses and committing to a program that can make the muscles in these areas stronger and more flexible is the basic tenet of any golf fitness program, which is why the assessment and correctives phases of your program are so important. I see a lot of senior golfers who struggle in so many areas that I often go right to correctives. Combined with a foam roller to help loosen your muscles, you can use these stretches as a guide to measure your progress and identify areas that may need extra attention, just as a Tour player would. I tell all my clients that you may not play like a Tour player, but you can get your body lose and prepared to play like one.

WALL MATRIX

For the first five correctives, your setup position will be the same. Start with your feet between 12 and 18 inches from the wall and your knees slightly flexed (mini squat), then lean back against the wall with your head, shoulders, and lower back flat against it. Do five repetitions for each corrective movement with each stretch equal to one deep breath.

1. FORWARD FLEXION

Slowly tilt your head forward until your chin touches your chest.

2. HORIZONTAL ROTATION

Rotate your head from side to side as far as you can while keeping your chin on the same plain as your starting position.

3. LATERAL EXTENSION

Tilt your head forward about two inches and stretch your right ear towards your right shoulder; repeat on your left side.

4. ELBOW SQUEEZE

Place your hands on your ears with your elbows out to the side and rotate your elbows forward, trying to touch them together in front of your nose.

5. ARM SLIDE

With your arms at your side and bent to 90 degrees at the elbows, lift your arms vertically while trying to keep your forearms pressed against the wall. If you struggle keeping them flat against the wall, try squeezing your shoulder blades together.

TUBING SEQUENCE

There are three levels of tubing tension: light, medium, and heavy resistance. The majority of golfers do best with medium tension, but if you're a beginner, start with the light version. Attach the tubing at approximately chest height to a stable object like a bannister or place one of the handles on the other side of a shut door, get in your posture, and perform one set of five repetitions with each arm.

6. ACROSS BODY

Hold the tubing in front of you with your elbow bent. Place a towel between your elbow and your side and rotate your arm across your midsection until it touches your ribs; return to the starting position.

7. AWAY FROM BODY

Hold the tubing in front of you with your elbow bent and your arm across your midsection. Place a towel between your elbow and your side and pull away from your body without allowing your elbow to separate from your side.

8. HIGH/LOW

With the resistance tubing anchored behind you, begin with your arm at a 90-degree angle and rotate your forearm forward until it's horizontal. Try to keep your elbow on the same plane as your shoulder.

9. LOW/HIGH

With the resistance tubing anchored in front of you, begin with your arm at a 90-degree angle and horizontal to the ceiling. Rotate your arm vertically as high as you can. Try to keep your elbow on the same plane as your shoulder.

MAT DRILLS

For the next six correctives, lie on your back with your knees bent and both feet on the ground, perform one set of five repetitions with each leg, holding each stretch for a long breath.

10. KNEE PUSH

Raise your right leg and push against your right knee with both hands. Try to create equal resistance with your arms and leg while you engage your abdominal muscles; switch legs.

11. HIP EXTENSIONS

Cross your right ankle over the left knee and rotate your lower body to the right. You can create additional stretch by pulling on your right arm and rotating your upper body to the left; switch legs.

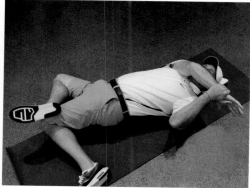

12. FIGURE-FOUR STRETCH

Cross your right ankle over your left knee and elevate both legs by grabbing your left thigh and pulling it toward your chest; switch legs.

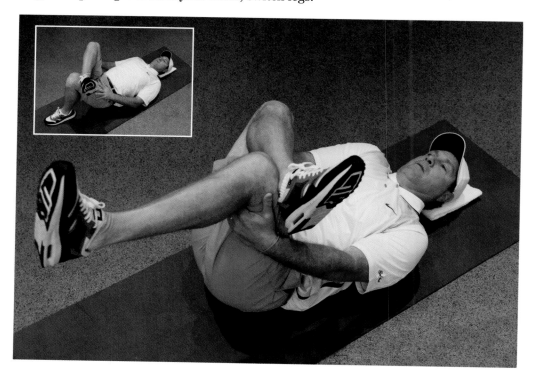

13. INTERNAL HIP ROTATION

Elevate your feet to 90 degrees with your knees bent. Place your hands between your knees and slowly rotate your lower legs out as far as they can go to feel a stretch in your hips.

14. CROSS-LEG BRIDGE

Cross your left foot over your right knee with your arms across your chest. Quickly push your hips up as high as you can; switch legs.

15. OPEN-BOOK ROTATION

Cross your left foot over your right knee and continue to rotate across your body toward the right. Stretch until your right thigh is parallel to the ground. Use your right hand to pull your knee down if need be. The goal is to keep your shoulders flat on the floor; switch legs.

KNEELING PATTERN

Begin on your hands and knees and do eight reps of each.

16. STRAIGHT-ARM LIFT

Extend one arm in front of you as high as you can. Try to keep your arm straight and on the same plane as your spine. Check to be sure you have the same range of motion with both arms; if not, add additional repetitions to the side with limited mobility.

17. VERTICAL-ELBOW LIFT

Place one hand behind your head while rotating your torso and elbow as high as you can. Try to point your elbow to the ceiling (it's okay to rotate your head with it). Like the Straight-Arm Lift, add additional repetitions to if you have limited mobility to one side.

18. TORSO ROTATION

Cross your arms over your chest, rotate into your backswing and follow-through with as much turn as possible. Try to keep your upper body in golf posture and your spine centered between your knees.

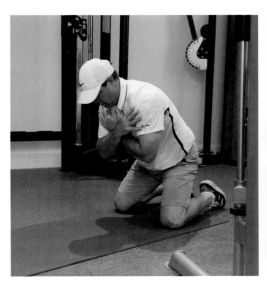 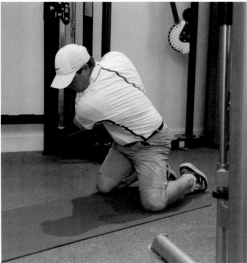

SEATED MOVEMENTS

The last two correctives are done from a seated position with your legs extended and your feet shoulder-width apart. Slowly perform one set of five repetitions, holding each stretch for two breaths.

19. TOE TOUCH

Begin with your arms across your chest to make sure you're centered, then reach forward and try to grab your toes. If you can't reach your toes without your knees bending, just reach forward as far as you can.

20. UPPER-BODY ROTATION

Extend your arms in front of you and rotate to each side. Try to keep your arms fully extended to increase your range of motion. The ultimate goal is to turn your chest 90 degrees without your arms bending.

SUMMARY

If you struggle with these correctives because of a lot of muscle tightness, you may want to incorporate weekly massages into your fitness routine at first. Nearly every Tour player receives multiple massages each week, with many employing their own personal masseuse who travels with them. I know a massage routine can be expensive, but perhaps you can join a massage club like Massage Envy. The work your therapist does in each session builds on itself. Your own masseuse who knows your body would be a big part of your team.

JONATHAN BYRD has the prototype frame for tournament golf. His fit and chiseled frame allows him to produce effortless power. A diligent gym guy, J. Byrd has already accumulated five Tour wins. After overcoming wrist surgery a few years back, shoulder and back strength has become a vital part of his plan. He also does pilates and yoga in the off season.

CHAPTER FOUR

MOBILITY

HOW WELL DOES YOUR BODY FUNCTION?

T HE NEXT TWO CHAPTERS will focus on improving your mobility and stability, which, by definition, are competing interests and yet crucial to any repeatable and efficient golf swing. Think of mobility and stability as two sides of a seesaw, with the ideal scenario being an equal amount of flexibility supported by the same amount of strength or stability. An example of this is when a female or junior player first learns the game. Because women and youngsters are generally more flexible but lack strength they have a tendency to over swing the golf club.

While that analogy is sound in general terms, the mobility side of the seesaw should receive more attention because your average male golfer will lose mobility at a greater rate than stability and it's more difficult to regain lost range of motion than it is to add strength. Many types of injuries, including back, hip, shoulder and knee issues, can rob you of much-needed mobility, as can external factors like your work environment. How often do you sit in your car or behind a desk. You do this long enough and eventually your body will lose its ability to turn and function properly, unless you take periodic stretching breaks during the day to counteract the effects. Loosely defined, mobility is a lack of muscle tightness that allows you to rotate your shoulders and hips properly and stay in your posture throughout the swing. Good mobility also allows you to create a differential between your hip and shoulder turns to create as much torque as possible in your swing.

Establishing your level of mobility and building a program that keeps you from becoming more restricted is the key to this chapter. Think of each of the following mobility exercises that Keith Mitchell, a former University of Georgia All-American, demonstrates as both assessment and remedy. The posture stretch, for example, will quickly identify the level of mobility you have in your shoulders and the rotation stretch is a measure of how much separation you can create between your shoulders and hips. Just as you practiced "rehearsal swings" with some of the assessments in Chapter Two, you'll want to perform the same posture and rotational assessments during your mobility program. Focusing on your golf posture and what your spine looks like will help you get into a more reliable and repeatable setup. I recommend doing these exercises before a round of golf, as well as prior to a workout. While a Stretching Pole, which I helped develop in the late-1990s, and a foam roller are useful for the following drills, they aren't necessary. A ball retriever or broom handle will work if you don't already have a Stretching Pole.

I haven't met a golfer yet who doesn't want to hit the ball farther. It's probably the reason why you're reading this book. While gaining strength and speed are most commonly associated with increased distance, maintaining your mobility, particularly for aging "desk jockeys" or those recovering from injury, is the most direct route to a more consistent and powerful golf swing.

This mobility routine that Keith demonstrates is a big reason why he finished third in driving distance on the 2016 Web.com Tour with an average of 320.7 yards per drive. Since he moved to Sea Island two years ago and began working together, his ball speed has jumped from 172 to 180 mph.

Start all of the mobility stretches with one set of five repetitions with the goal of advancing to 10 reps as you become more comfortable.

STRETCHING-POLE DRILLS

This is a valuable sequence. You'll see Tour players not only doing this in the gym, but also on the driving range prior to hitting balls.

POSTURE STRETCH

With the pole in front of you at a slight angle, grab the end with both hands and push down with your shoulders, keeping your hips back while elongating your spine and holding the stretch for one long breath. To increase your mobility, push your arms from side-to-side to allow for additional stretch in your lats.

ROTATION SIDE STRETCH

From your golf posture with the Stretching Pole resting on your right shoulder, simulate a backswing by extending both arms to the right. Ideally, you should turn your shoulders 90 degrees while turning your hips away from your extended arms. Think of turning around your spine; repeat on left side.

CHEST-AND-HIPS STRETCH

From your golf posture with the Stretching Pole to your right, hold the top of the pole with your right hand and your arm extended to the side. With your left hand on your right hip, slowly rotate your hips away from your raised arm maintaining your golf posture. Try to create as much "separation" between your extended arm and your hips; repeat on left side.

FOAM-ROLLER SEQUENCE

Using a 36-inch roller, do these exercises as quickly as possible.

HIP MOBILITY

With a foam roller about six inches in front of you and hands by your ears, alternate lifting each leg over the roller as quickly as you can while focusing on your balance. The goal is to see how many reps you can do without losing your balance with either your leg coming from inside to outside or vice-versa.

GOLF POSTURE/ALTERNATE-ARM REACH

Setup with both hands on top of the roller and reach back with one arm and then the other. Try to complete 180 degrees of extension to ensure you're turning your shoulders 90 degrees while keeping your lower body stable to create greater separation.

STRAIGHT-ARM LIFT

Place both hands on top of the roller, reach straight up with one arm and then the other. The goal is to align your arm with your spine angle while keeping your elbow straight. Limit your range of motion on the first few repetitions until you establish a pattern and then add speed as you progress.

FOAM-ROLLER RECOVERY

These next two movements are great to help create blood flow in what are often tight, restricted areas. Take your time on these and know that there are days you'll need to spend more time doing them.

HIP-AND-IT-BAND ROLL OUT

Lay on your side with the foam roller under your IT band (iliotibial band or upper leg) and "roll" on your leg from just above your knee to your hip; switch legs.

MID-BACK/T-SPINE ROLL OUT

Lay on your back with the roller positioned just below your shoulders, roll down the length of your back by pushing out with your legs.

DAVID TOMS is a special golfer. A major winner and three-decade-long player, DT has a smooth and steady swing and demeanor. He is consistent with his lower back conditioning and has been competitive through out his forties. Looking for big results on the Champions Tour in the years to come.

CHAPTER FIVE

STABILITY

HOW TO BALANCE YOUR
FLEXIBILITY AND STRENGTH

A LTHOUGH MOBILITY is the more crucial side of the golf swing seesaw, it's your stability that will dictate if you can efficiently transfer the energy you've created through a full turn and proper separation between your shoulders and hips into the golf ball.

The average club-head speed on the PGA Tour is 112 mph, and that balloons to 122 mph for bombers like Dustin Johnson. Controlling that force in a balanced and stable way is as important as being able to produce that power. This symbiotic relationship became a talking point in early 2016 when Golf Channel analyst Brandel Chamblee voiced concerns over Rory McIlroy's fitness program, specifically the Northern Irishman's "extensive weightlifting" and the possibility it could lead to injury. McIlroy responded with a video posted to social media doing squats, later explaining his primary fitness goals were to remain injury-free as well as gain strength. For McIlroy, who is among the strongest and most flexible players on Tour, being able to control the golf club depends on the stability that his legs and core can provide. Gary Player said it best, most of those who don't understand the value of an exercise component to golf often make the misconception that it's going to do damage. The reality is through today's checks and balances, through functional assessment, just about any player can benefit from proper training and a weightlifting program.

While the idea of controlling your club head during a swing is appealing, in practical terms improving your stability will help keep you from swaying and shifting your center of gravity during your golf swing. I estimate that the best players in the world move one to two degrees off the ball laterally during the backswing, but they don't sway like so many amateurs. They also can stick their finish like an Olympic gymnast unlike the signature "falling away" move of most weekend players. While thicker, muscular players whom I like to call "medicine ball" body types generally struggle with mobility, thinner golfers—"Stretching Pole" types—normally have to be aware of the need for increased stability.

Cory Whitsett, the 2007 U.S. Junior Amateur champion whom I began working with while he was an All-American at the University of Alabama, is an example of the stability needed to control extraordinary mobility. Cory is a typical Stretching Pole player with hyper-mobility that caused strain and eventual back problems earlier in his career. Through our work together, the 25-year-old is slowly being "built" into more of a medicine ball player so as to improve the symmetry of his swing. We focus on squats and core work to get really stable in the lower body and it's really helped his swing. Cory had a stress reaction in his low back after his junior year of high school, but he hasn't had any issues since we started working together. Before that, he hadn't spent much if any time working out, but he now realizes that a better body leads to better golf. Through essentially the same program outlined in this chapter and demonstrated by Cory, he has improved his core and leg strength, eliminated his back issues, and gained distance. These functional stability movements better enable him to control his golf swing while building his frame to prepare for the next decade. Cory is a lot like Dustin Johnson, whom I worked with earlier in his career, a long and lean player who could generate enormous amounts of energy but needed the stability to control it and avoid injury. The good news for players who test poorly in the stability phase of my assessment is it's easier to gain strength than it is to improve flexibility. But the balance between the two elements for an efficient and powerful swing is crucial, which is why the mobility and stability training programs were designed to allow every player, regardless of skill or physical ability, to begin immediately.

Chamblee's concerns over McIlroy's workout program were certainly valid, albeit slightly misinformed. Maintaining the symmetry between strength and flexibility is the challenge faced by every golfer and the overriding goal of this book. Stability and mobility have to develop hand-and-hand and it's a constant check and balance. If you are going to work out with weights, you always need to be careful to maintain your flexibility.

As a Nike staffer, and I was asked by Rory's swing coach, Mike Bannon, to take a look at Rory's swing in 2013 after he missed the cut at The Open Championship at Muirfield and was struggling with his game a little. A lot of people were blaming his switch from Titleist clubs and balls to Nike equipment that year, and that adjustment period might have been a small part of it, but I think his problem was really due to decreased flexibility. He was about a year into his heavy lifting program and was starting to have some issues with his full swing, particularly with the driver. Basically, the length of his backswing was about 12 degrees shorter, which was due to his increased amount of muscle mass. In my opinion, the upper-body strength he had gained caused a tightening in his lats, so he wasn't able to complete his backswing, which affected his timing. So, after consulting with his team, we just increased his flexibility program with the help of one of my Stretching Poles. He regained his flexibility—and his game—in a matter of weeks if not days.

Because of Rory's incredible athleticism, he is able to lift a little more weight than most people, but for most golfers my philosophy on weight training is to use lighter weights with higher repetitions, combining multiple exercises that challenge your aerobic and anaerobic (short exertion, high intensity) capacities. Lifting too much heavy weight could change your swing; lighter weights will maintain your pliability as you slowly gain strength, allowing the muscles to develop more properly as it relates to your golf swing.

The first five movements use a Bosu ball, which is a great piece of equipment that is highly specific to the golf swing. Repeat 8-10 times with each leg. Maintain your balance throughout.

ONE-ARM REACH LUNGE

This exercise combines both a stability and mobility challenge. Start from a standing position with your arms across your chest and lunge forward onto a Bosu ball while reaching back with one arm. Reach back from the same side you are lunging from (right leg forward, right arm back); switch legs and arms.

LATERAL SQUAT ARMS CROSSED

From your golf posture with your arms across your chest, "load" into your left leg while extending your right leg laterally. Be sure your knee stays centered over your foot; switch legs.

LATERAL SQUAT TORSO ROTATION

Like the lateral squat, you will step laterally from your golf posture but will add a shoulder turn as you step. Turn toward the direction you are stepping, which will allow you to feel yourself loading into your back and legs like a golf swing; switch legs.

ONE-LEG BALANCE/ONE-ARM REACH

This motion will be challenging, especially if you do it on an upside-down Bosu ball.
Balance yourself on your right leg and slowly reach back with your right arm.
The goal is to turn your shoulders as you would in the golf swing.
Use a medicine ball to help you balance; switch legs.

MEDICINE BALL ONE-LEG TORSO ROTATION

Standing on your right leg on an upside-down Bosu ball, hold a medicine ball to your chest and turn your shoulders to the right. Keep your turn short initially and slowly lengthen with each repetition. As you become more comfortable with the motion, extend the medicine ball away from your chest to create a greater turn; switch legs.

The following three exercises utilize a kettle bell, which range in weight from 10-50 pounds. Use the weight that allows you to do 8-10 repetitions comfortably, which for a beginner would be about 20 or 25 pounds.

ONE-ARM SQUAT TO STAND

From a squat position hold the kettle bell with one arm and stand straight up. Be sure to maintain correct posture by pulling your shoulders back and engaging your glutes; switch arms.

TWO-ARM POSTURE SQUAT

From a standing position with feet shoulder-with apart, hold a kettle bell with both hands across your chest and squat. Your goal is to get your thighs parallel to the ground before returning to a standing position.

ONE-LEG OPPOSITE TOE TOUCH

Standing on your left leg hold a kettle bell in your right hand, bend at the waist, and reach for your left foot. The goal is to maintain your posture and use your lower body to initiate the motion. You may have to perform this motion without any weight to start; switch legs and arms.

The final four exercises are done with a stability ball, which range in size from 55-75 centimeters in diameter. Generally, the taller you are, the bigger the ball, but check the box for your correct size. Do 8 to 10 reps for each.

ROTATIONAL SWING

From your golf posture hold the ball in front of you and turn into your backswing and follow through. Try to maintain a stable lower body with as little hip turn as possible while creating extension in your back swing and follow through.

CIRCULAR ROTATION ("THE BIG CIRCLE")

From your golf posture hold the ball at 12 o'clock and rotate it clockwise in a complete circle. Focus on maintaining your golf posture with your shoulders back; repeat in a counter-clockwise motion.

SEATED MEDICINE BALL ROTATION

Sit on the ball and hold a medicine ball with your arms extended in front of you. Rotate your arms to the left and right while keeping your arms straight and extended away from your torso.

SEATED ONE-LEG OUT ROTATION

In the same position as above, raise your right leg to create an unbalanced position and turn toward the extended leg. Focus on maintaining your balance. You may need to brace the back of the stability ball against a wall to help you complete this motion; switch legs.

SUMMARY

You've just completed a stability workout that dozens of Tour players use on a regular basis. As this program becomes easier, you can add repetitions, weight, and speed with the ultimate goal of completing this routine in less than 10 minutes.

ZACH JOHNSON is a tremendous example of an over achiever. His focus and discipline never wavers. Over the years, Zach has improved his aerobic conditioning and range of motion. He is a benchmark for consistency in the fitness center, never misses a day of workouts.

CHAPTER SIX

BALANCE

MYTH BUSTING AND STRENGTHENING
YOUR FOUNDATION

Nothing reveals your physical limitations like a golf swing because it affects just about every part of your body. You can play this game for a long time, and play it fairly well, by working around your limitations. But as Clint Eastwood said in *Dirty Harry*, "A man has got to know his limitations." In order to really improve, you've got to know how your body moves or, rather, doesn't move. Slicers, for instance, are typically one-side dominant. They're able to make a decent backswing, but their lack of symmetry and mobility leads to the over-the-top curse.

But unlike many other sports, there are no one-size-fits-all models that can be used to predict greatness in golf. Golf swings are as varied and unique as the courses themselves, and success is regularly born from unorthodox swings. There is, however, an underlying physiological thread that connects nearly every world-class player. Of all the things a PGA Tour player can do—carry the ball 300 yards, get up-and-down at will, convert an endless line of six-foot putts—it's his ability to pass a basic, relatively straightforward balance assessment that connects them all. Tour players and high-level amateurs, without exception, pass all three tests below every time. Generally, your recreational golfer, even good recreational golfers, fail one if not all three. Not only is my three-step test a part of my basic assessment of all my athletes, it's a fundamental component of any balanced golf swing. It's also the cornerstone of any pre-round warm up.

In the first drill, Zach Johnson, or any Tour pro for that matter, has no trouble standing on one leg, turning their upper body, and extending an arm behind them with their eyes closed, and they can do that all-day long. I can't get one recreational player to stand for very long on one leg, let alone close their eyes and turn. The one thing a Tour player has over a recreational golfer is better balance, bar none. I've never seen a good player go through my assessment with bad balance. People say, "That's not even fitness." Oh, yes, it is. Now is it muscular or neuromuscular? It depends, but the good news is balance can be trained. One of the best drills for people who don't finish their golf swing is one I learned long ago from the legendary teacher Bob Toski: Turn to the top of your backswing and balance on one leg. Balance is the most important aspect in golf because it's a two-sided sport. You're stationary yet moving. If you don't have balance in your feet and all the way up the chain, it becomes very apparent that completing your swing will be very difficult. The reason why balance is so important, generally speaking, is that recreational golfers have a decent back swing, regardless of their ability to play, but their impact and through swings are normally out-of-balance and therefore they can't rotate correctly and hold their finish position. The majority of amateur golfers don't have adequate "proprioception," or awareness of the position of your body. This inability leads to a swing that's out of balance or, put another way, isn't symmetrical, which means the backswing is not on the same plane as their follow through.

The basic assessment that follows is the tie that binds nearly every great golfer, so much so that the majority of the elite players I work with use these drills as part of their daily warm-up. Think of this assessment as the most fundamental way to assure your body is prepared to play golf, as well as a snapshot of areas that may require extra attention.

Zach does it every day to make sure he's not losing any of his turning ability. A Tour pro with a diminished turn is an unemployed Tour pro. Although most will view players like Dustin Johnson and Billy Horschel as the quintessential athlete-golfer, Zach is a much better example of what a detailed and dedicated fitness program can do for the average player's game. I put him through a similar assessment when he first came to see me at PGA National in the late 1990s looking for ways to improve his game and his body. He called me from the parking lot afterward and told me he couldn't put his car in drive he was so sore. It can be very demanding if you're not used to it. Since then, however, Zach has become one of the Tour's most "functionally" strong players, if not the most imposing at 5-foot-10, 164 pounds. Anyone can benefit from a sustained workout or training program. In Zach's case, he was a good athlete, but he didn't have a strong fitness program. From our first meeting, he realized he needed to get his body ready to compete more regularly and it's a big reason why he's won two majors: the 2007 Masters and the 2015 Open Championship at St. Andrews.

To illustrate how dedicated he is and how important a better body is to better golf, the week he won the Open at St. Andrews, we flew into Scotland on a charter from the John Deere Classic the Monday morning of tournament week. He had just finished T3 at the John Deere and was playing well. The first thing we did when we got to St. Andrews was go to the gym at The Old Course Hotel. He also worked out Tuesday and Wednesday, as well. Continuing his good play, he opened with a 66—one stroke behind leader Dustin Johnson. A second-round 71 left him T4, three shots off the lead. But when 50-mph winds suspended the third round for much the day, we knew the odds of him playing were very small because of his late tee time. So we did a full workout in the morning, which included all of our strength training but with lighter weights, along with some of the stretching and movement exercises outlined in this book. Then, when he was sure he wasn't playing that day, we went back later that day and went through all of our assessment and evaluation work like he does in this chapter. We got two workouts in the middle of the tournament. He finally got to practice a little at 8:30 pm when the winds died down. He felt really good on Sunday, shooting a 70 that left him three strokes off the lead and T6 going into the final round on Monday. But because of that mid-tournament workout session, he was one of the freshest guys in the field and shot another 66 to force a four-hole aggregate playoff with Louis Oosthuizen and Marc Leishman, which he won by one stroke. Having the ability to adapt and change is important, as is taking advantage of a window of opportunity to get in a workout at the Tour level.

The first three drills of Zach's warm-up routine in this chapter comprise the balance assessment. One thing I've learned is that most right-handed Tour players have great balance on their right leg, but even better balance or stability on their left leg. They're hitting into that side, so they've got to have better balance because they're basically slamming the door on that side. It gives them the advantage of being able to keep their spine angle back through impact and not get in front of the ball, a common mistake amateurs make.

Performed correctly with your eyes closed, these assessments are extremely difficult and will take time to perfect, but they will provide a regular baseline to measure your progress. Combined with the other elements of this warm-up routine, they will assure your body is really prepared to perform its best on the course.

The first three movements comprise the assessment phase.

SINGLE-LEG BALANCE

From your golf posture with your arms folded across your chest, stand on one leg and try to "reach" your chest over your toes and hold that position for three breaths. The goal is to execute these drills with your eyes closed while visualizing what you're doing, but you may need to start with your eyes open and stand near a wall or countertop for a little help balancing. Switch legs and repeat.

SINGLE-LEG BALANCE ROTATION

From your golf posture with your arms folded across your chest, raise your left leg and turn your left shoulder over your right toe. Hold for three breaths. Repeat the drill with your right leg elevated, turning your right shoulder over your left toe and holding for three breaths. For a greater challenge, add a one arm vertical reach as illustrated by Zach.

SINGLE-LEG BALANCE STRAIGHT-ARM REACH

This is the "pro" version of the warm-up after you've mastered the first two. Starting from the same position as above, extend your arms while you turn to the right with your left hand reaching for your right toe. Hold for three breaths. The goal would be to have both arms aligned with your centerline or beyond; switch legs and reach for your left toe with your right hand.

Now that you've improved your balance, here are Zach's final four dynamic movements that he does with tubing prior to each round. Perform 8 to 10 repetitions for each one as fast as possible.

SPLIT-STANCE ROW

From a lunge or split-stance position with the tubing attached at chest height, alternately pull each arm toward your chest allowing the middle of your back to piston as you pull. To increase difficulty, balance only on your front leg.

SINGLE-ARM PUNCH

From your golf posture with the tubing to the side, hold both ends at your stomach and punch to the right with your left arm. Try to create 90 degrees of shoulder turn while keeping your hips facing forward. Turn around to repeat this drill with your right hand and a punch to the left.

TUBING EXPLOSIVE SQUAT

This is similar to the "squat" assessment. Stand on the resistance tubing and hold the handles just above your shoulders, "load" your squat, and push up. This is a really great exercise to rev up the power in your legs before your round.

LATERAL TUBING SHUFFLE

With the tubing under your feet, hold both handles about waist high with your palms facing up. Stand up straight and make an aggressive step laterally one way and then back the other.

SUMMARY

Since Zach moved to Sea Island eight years ago, he's won 10 times on Tour, including two majors. I can't say how much a pleasure it is to work with a pro like Zach. He's also been a great role model for young PGA Tour players I train, like Brian Harmon, J.T. Poston, and Patton Kizzire.

CHAPTER SEVEN

BASIC STRENGTH PLAN

SOME MIGHT MAKES RIGHT

W HEN IT COMES TO ADDING MUSCLE MASS, I like to stress dumbbells and cables over machines and power lifting because there's no correlation between the latter and hitting the ball farther or more effectively. In many cases, the injury potential is so much greater that I really don't want anyone doing power lifting without supervision. A club weighs less than two pounds, so the notion that I'm going to hit a golf ball better if I do five sets of 200-pound deadlifts isn't accurate. There's no research that it will. It might help, but the reality is the risk of injury while you're lifting is so much higher because most amateurs are not bilaterally symmetrical. One side is better than the other. Why do back injuries occur? Because one side of your body is pulling more of the load. Same with using a barbell. Now if you're hyper-mobile like Rory or Dustin and you test out in all the assessments like a five-star athlete, certainly there's a place for that. The best example of someone who should be lifting more is a high school or college athlete who is super flexible and wants to put on more size. But the lifting should take place as far as possible from your round of golf.

I get this question a lot from my amateurs: how much power lifting do Tour players do? The answer is they will do it in the off-season because they have more time to recover when they're breaking muscles down lifting heavier weights. There are examples of high-level golfers who lifted their swing away like Keith Clearwater, who won twice in his rookie year of 1987. In the 1990s, Clearwater was at the forefront of pros who started

RSM
CLASSIC

4

Par   5
Yards   590

BRIAN HARMAN maybe the most explosive golfer on Tour. A natural right hander who plays lefty, "Harms" was a can't miss wonder kid. A two-time Walker Cup player, he immediately made waves on the PGA Tour with his expanded skill set. From a functional standpoint, he's one of the best athletes in the game.

to do more weightlifting. Labeled "the leading iron pumper on the PGA Tour," the Utah pro was lifting heavy weights five or six days a week, adding 22 pounds of muscle to his six-foot frame. But as his strength increased, his swing became short and quick and his earnings decreased. He was off the Tour altogether by 1995.

If you're going to lift, you should be doing the assessments in Chapter Two within every workout because they're giving you the golf-centric motion patterns to play good golf. With my pros, we do a power day, a speed and agility day, and a functional day. During the season, power comprises 10 percent of the workout time, speed and agility 30 percent, and functional 60 percent. Off-season, it may look the opposite, 60-20-20.

Billy Horschel, the posterchild for fitness on the PGA Tour, recently built a state-of-the-art gym in his north Florida home with a big University of Florida Gators' logo on the floor. Brandt Snedeker, Charles Howell III, and the vast majority of top players also have elaborate home gyms that rival even the most comprehensive commercial work-out facilities. I realize most people don't have those kinds of resources, but that doesn't mean you can't create your own gym specific to your fitness program that is as convenient as it is cost-effective. For less than $400, about the cost of a year's membership at a local gym, you can create an area in your home that is tailored to your specific goals. The biggest reason is convenience. Make it as easy as you can on yourself. There's no need to put on your workout clothes, get in your car, drive to the gym, and then wait for machines to open up. All you need is a dedicated space that you can pop in an out during the day to do as many exercises as you have time for—10 minutes at a time. That's it. These aren't strenuous routines either, so you don't have to fret about doing them. That whole "no pain, no gain" thing does not hold true.

The basic elements of the home gym would include a stability ball, resistance tubing, dumbbells, a Bosu ball, a Stretching Pole, some medicine balls, and a foam roller. While next-generation functional training machines—like the cable systems found in most modern gyms—allow athletes to train not just specific muscles, but to do so at specific angles that can be scaled to extremely golf-specific motions, most of these same exercises can be performed with resistance tubing and dumbbells for a fraction of the cost.

Resistance tubing was first developed as a therapy product and generally comes in three "weights"—light, medium, and heavy. It's important to find the resistance level that you're comfortable with. Zach, one of the most functionally strongest players on Tour, yet uses medium resistance tubing for many of his exercises and for the majority of recreational golfers, medium-weight tubing is more than enough to create a challenging and effective motion. For most recreational golfers, 3- to 8-pound dumbbells will do, which you can increase to 10- to 15-pound weights as you advance, while a 6- or

FOR LESS THAN $400, ABOUT THE COST OF A YEAR'S MEMBERSHIP AT A LOCAL GYM, YOU CAN CREATE AN AREA IN YOUR HOME THAT IS TAILORED TO YOUR SPECIFIC GOALS. THE BIGGEST REASON IS CONVENIENCE.

8-pound medicine ball should suffice.

Foam rollers vary in firmness and length, so you'll want to pick the one that's right for you. They're the one piece of equipment that players take on Tour. It often replaces the need for a massage.

Without access to an assortment of high-tech machines for a lower-body workout you can create the same motions and benefits through various lunges, lateral squatting, and presses; bridging and planking are perfect to work your core without putting too much strain on your back. Those of you who travel for a living will need to be a little more creative, but even the most basic hotel gyms have some collection of dumbbells and a stability ball that you can use for an effective and efficient workout. If not, there are plenty of exercises in this book you can do in your hotel room without any equipment.

You'll also want to assure you have enough space in your home gym for your stretching and mobility exercises, which are a crucial part of any golf-specific fitness program. To maintain the balance of the mobility/stability seesaw you'll want to regularly check your flexibility during your workout. In between exercises you should stretch the appropriate muscle group. If you're in the middle of a chest pull, for example, you'll want to stretch your latissimus dorsi (mid-back) between each set.

The vast majority of exercises in this book will use lighter weights and you should think of your first repetition as a "practice swing," where you trace the line of the intended movement and then increase the speed with each repetition. You will also want to be sure to always check your posture, alignment, and that your hips are back, just as you would with your golf swing.

You can start your workout program immediately regardless of how you tested out in your assessments. This is a shovel-ready plan you can begin at home now. Most importantly, take an extra 10 or 15 minutes to visit your home gym every time before you head to the course or the range. You'll be amazed at how much better you'll play by getting your body ready properly before you tee it up.

The first eight exercises require two light-weight dumbbells. Begin with eight repetitions and increase the number of reps as you become more comfortable.

SQUAT SHOULDER PRESS

With your hands on your shoulders and your feet shoulder-width apart, squat as deep as you can (like you're lining up a putt) and as you stand, press the dumbbells vertically over your head.

SQUAT PRESS STAND

Same as above but here you do the press before you stand. If you have difficulty keeping your heels on the ground, place a block under your heels to allow for more range of motion.

LATERAL LUNGE AND CURL

With the dumbbells at your side and your feet together in a standing position, step laterally right and left about a yard while keeping your inside leg straight. As you step, "hammer" curl the dumbbells (palms facing toward each other). This is a speed exercise and should be completed as quickly as possible.

TOE TOUCH TO UPRIGHT ROW

From a standing position with the dumbbells at your side, bend at the waist and try to touch the ground with the weights. As you rise back up, pull your hands to your chin keeping your elbows away from your shoulders.

FORWARD LUNG AND CURL

From a standing position with the dumbbells in front of your thighs, step forward into a comfortable depth that allows you to maintain your balance and perform a hammer curl. Be sure to keep an upright posture as you alternate legs.

SPLIT STANCE ALTERNATE PUNCH

From a lunge position with the dumbbells pulled in close to your chest, alternate extending each hand across your chest like you're boxing. This is a "go-to" exercise for Tour players because it encourages a constant connection, like the golf swing, and engages your arms, core, chest, and legs.

BACKSWING TO IMPACT

This is a three-part motion that begins in your golf posture while holding a dumbbell in both hands at your normal address position. Rotate into your backswing allowing the weight to help you make a full turn and return to impact position. Do all eight repetitions before changing sides.

SINGLE-LEG BALANCE SWINGS

Same as above but here you're balanced on your right leg as you turn to the right and your left leg as you turn to the left.

The next six exercises utilize resistance tubing. Begin with five repetitions and increase the number of reps as you become more comfortable.

GOLF POSTURE ONE-ARM ROTATIONAL PULL BACK

From your golf posture with the resistance tubing anchored in front of you at about waist height, pull back with one arm while trying to keep your arm on the same plane as your shoulders. Be sure to check your golf posture while executing this motion; switch arms.

ROTATIONAL CHOPS

From your golf posture with the resistance tubing anchored to your side, hold the tubing in both hands at waist height and pull just past your impact position. Be sure to turn your hips and keep your spine angle stable during this motion; switch sides.

ONE-ARM ACROSS-CHEST PULL

From the same starting position, hold the tubing in one arm in front and slowly extend that arm out to shoulder height. Be sure to maintain your golf posture throughout the motion and don't let your arm get above your shoulder.

BACKSWING

From the same starting position, turn to the top of your backswing with both hands on the handle. Be sure to rotate your shoulders and hands as far as you can until you feel the stretch in your upper back and slowly lower the tubing back to your address position; repeat on non-dominant side.

DOWNSWING

From your golf posture with the resistance tubing anchored behind you, allow the tubing to take you to the top of your backswing. Be sure to get your shoulder under your chin and your hands as high as they would be in your normal backswing position before pulling down to your impact position. The resistance will increase as you pull the tubing down.

VERTICAL-ARM LUNGE

With the resistance tubing anchored behind you at waist height, hold your arms over your head and alternate stepping forward into a lunge position with your right and left legs. Be sure to keep your arms straight over your head and focus on stretching your shoulders and lats.

For the final three routines, you'll need a medicine ball and a step-up bench. Begin with five repetitions on both your right and left sides and increase the number of reps as you become more comfortable.

BENCH STEP-UP ARM LIFT

With your left foot on the raised bench, step up while you raise your right knee to 90 degrees and your arms overhead. Use a 6- to 8-pound medicine ball for resistance and increase the speed as you become more comfortable while maintaining your balance; switch legs.

BENCH STEP-UP TORSO ROTATION

As above but add a horizontal rotation with your upper body toward the raised leg with the ball in front of your chest; switch legs.

SIDE-BENCH SHUFFLE/TORSO ROTATION

Begin with one foot on the bench and as you step across it alternating legs, rotate your upper body toward the leg that is on the ground. Focus on turning your shoulders and upper body while limiting your hip turn.

SUMMARY

This is pretty the same routine Brandt Snedeker used during the 2012 Open Championship at Royal Lytham where he finished T3. The gym we were using in town didn't have any of the modern equipment like we do here, so we had to stick to the basics during his workouts that week and it opened our eyes. After he tied the 36-hole scoring record at The Open with rounds of 66 and 64, we were walking into the gym on Friday afternoon, and he looked at me and said, "Let's just stick to the basics. It seems to be working." Many times, people are looking for the next big thing, but sometimes the basics work the best. In other words, this doesn't have to be complicated.

CHAPTER EIGHT

ADVANCED STRENGTH PLAN

STEPPING UP YOUR WEIGHT-LIFTING PROGRAM

STRENGTH
CARDIO
FLEXIBILITY

Y OU'D HEARD OF THE FOOD PYRAMID, RIGHT? Well, there's a golf workout pyramid, too, but instead of the fruit-and-vegetables base, flexibility is on the bottom, with cardio replacing whole grains and dairy products in the middle, and strength training at the top where red meat, butter, and high glycemic foods like cookies reside. Traditional strength training has always been more of a question mark. Leave the bodybuilding to bodybuilders and opt for functional strength training like I've outlined in the last chapter and this one. Your improvement in golf is based solely on your functionality. You can't improve in golf simply by getting stronger. Functional strength is defined as the

PATTON KIZZIRE is one of the tallest golfers on Tour. At 6'5" PK towers over most competitors. With a smooth swing and controlled rhythm, he is having success early in his career. The 2015 Web.com player of the year is a tireless worker in the gym, keeping his legs and core strong. Big things are on the horizon for Patton.

ability to run your load-joints (shoulders, hips, knees, and ankles) through a full range of motion without pain, stiffness, or restriction. Years ago, when we were an agrarian society, we got our functional strength naturally through pushing and pulling farm equipment around, but in today's world where we sit at a desk all day, talk on the phone, and lie around watching sports on TV, it's vital we find ways to keep our load-bearing architecture healthy.

Tour players apply the golf pyramid to their weekly schedules, doing their heavy lifting on Monday and their functional training on Tuesday and Wednesday. Once the tournament starts, it's primarily flexibility and speed. Even though amateurs typically only play one day a week on the weekends, their routine should follow that model, which I call the ABCs of golf: Monday is Aggressive when you push your muscles to exhaustion with more challenging weights, midweek is for Biomechanics and assessments to make sure you haven't lost any mobility from your strength training, and the end of the week is for Cardio and stretching to get your body as consistent and symmetrical as possible prior to playing.

The two forms of cardio programs, duration and interval, are what players use during a tournament week. In the duration plan, they'll stay on a treadmill or stationary bike for 15 to 25 minutes, typically after their workout earlier in the week to build heart and lung stamina. The interval segment is a shorter, high-intensity session about 25 percent as long and is done prior to stretching and hitting the range before their round.

However you label it, the concept of power training as it applies to golf is probably vastly different than what most people imagine. This chapter is about building stability and strength while at the same time maintaining your mobility and range of motion. Although there are a limitless number of power programs you can create from the most basic equipment, this workout is virtually identical to the programs performed by dozens of PGA Tour players each week in the mobile onsite fitness trailer. It's an in-season program that's designed to let you build some muscle yet still perform on the golf course. As one of my players, Patton Kizzire, who finished 72nd on the money list his rookie year on Tour in 2015-16, demonstrates in this chapter, this is an advanced fitness program for an athletic golfer.

I've been working with Patton for the past five years, the first three of which he was bouncing around the mini-tours. But then one morning in 2012 when I was training Davis Love III at his house in the off-season, my phone rang and it was Patton who wanted to know if he could get in a training session in before he went home to Auburn later that day. When I told him I was busy, Davis immediately offered to have him join us. Patton couldn't have been more honored by the opportunity, especially after Davis sat down with him afterward and asked him about his career goals. That's when Patton decided he needed to move to Sea Island, commit himself to a comprehensive fitness program, and soak up the influence of the more than 15 top pros who live here, like Matt Kuchar, Jonathan Byrd and Harris English, who are collectively known as the "Sea Island mafia." It was a huge turning point for him and his career, culminating with his winning the Web.com Tour Player of the Year Award in 2015.

Unlike power programs in most other sports, for golf it's best to focus on speed and form with less weight during your workouts. In golf training, we move at a more rapid pace than you would in a more general power program because you're trying to move at a pace similar to a golf swing speed and your breathing rhythm. The average pace of a golf swing is between 1.2 and 1.4 seconds, which is roughly how long it takes you to take a single breath and, ideally, how long it should take you to perform a single repetition in this power program. The goal for each exercise is to perform 12-15 repetitions, which means you'll want to use a weight that allows you to complete the exercise with a consistent motion without compromising your form or posture as you become fatigued.

This program can also be easily "scaled" depending on a player's abilities. A beginner, for example, would likely start with the first six exercises and gradually build up, adding some of the others as they become more comfortable. The concept is to build stamina and consistency, and the best way to do that is to start slow and gradually work your way up. As you become more comfortable with the program, you'll want to add the assessment protocols from Chapter Two to your power program to maintain your mobility and flexibility as you progress. The hip stretch in this program is an example of an assessment I've added that allows you to focus on areas where you may need improvement and to keep the workout as golf specific as possible. In fact, each of the power exercises that follow has an assessment addition. After completing the "Overhead Triceps" exercise, for example, you'll want to do the "Arms Overhead Horizontal Reach" assessment, especially if you struggled with that assessment. The assessments are designed to stretch the same muscles you just strengthened and will also allow you to eliminate soreness from your workout and go straight to the golf course afterward, which would be difficult after a traditional power program workout.

Individual body types will want to alter their program to fit their needs. Kizzire is a Stretching Pole type player whose program is focused on creating more stability in his core and lower body. His program allows him to spend extra time on those areas during his workouts. Tailored programs mean better body control, which leads to better control of your golf ball. A better body allows you to consistently transfer the energy and power.

This power workout can also be adjusted for an off-season program during the winter months. By splitting the workout—the first six exercises (along with your assessment drills) one day followed by the remaining 13 the next—and increasing to two sets for each exercise, you can alternate days and work different muscles. You may also need to adjust your program to assure proper symmetry. In golf, both sides of the body must function at the same level to produce the best results, and many of the exercises in this chapter will require you to train your dominant and non-dominant sides even if that means using no weights or resistance at first.

While power is the ultimate goal of this chapter, it's important to understand that in golf terms that means more speed and consistency, not more weight.

The first six exercises are done with a cable machine, but you can also use tubing. Perform one set of 12 to 15 repetitions in golf posture or 6 to 8 reps on each leg from a split stance.

CHEST FLY

From a split stance with your spine titled forward and the cables set at shoulder height, extend your arms to the side and push forward in front of your chest. Maintain a horizontal plane and keep the arms nearly extended. If you struggle with a split stance, you can change to your golf posture.
ASSESSMENT: Vertical Press (No. 3). On page 29.

ROWS

From a split stance with either leg forward while facing a cable machine set at shoulder height, pull the handle to your side while reaching with your opposite arm. Try to keep your arms on a horizontal plane; switch arms.

ASSESSMENT: Straight-Arm Push/One-Arm Lift (No. 2). On page 29.

TRICEPS

From a split stance or golf posture with the cable set as high as it will go, hold a cable rope with both hands and press down. Performing this exercise on a single leg forces your body to stay centered and better isolates the triceps. Try to keep your elbows stationary by your side as you press down.

ASSESSMENT: Forward Lunge/Vertical-Arm Lift (No. 5). On page 30.

PULLS

Facing the machine in your golf posture with the cable set high, hold a cable rope with both hands and your arms extended from your shoulders. Keep your arms straight as you pull your hands to your thighs. Add a core element to this exercise by alternately pulling to each leg.

ASSESSMENT: Straight-Arm Torso Rotation (No. 10). On page 33.

OVERHEAD TRICEPS

From a split stance with your back to the machine and the cable set high, hold a cable rope with both hands with your elbows bent to 90 degrees in front of your face. Extend both arms at the same time until they are horizontal to the ground.

ASSESSMENT: Arms Overhead Horizontal Reach (No. 4). On page 30.

CHOPS

From your golf posture to the side of the machine set at waist height, hold a single cable with both hands and pull both arms down to impact position while maintaining your spine angle and keeping both feet on the ground; switch sides.

ASSESSMENT: Straight-Arm Lunge Rotation (No. 12). On page 34.

The next four lifts on are done lying on a bench or stability ball using 25-pound dumbbells as a good starting weight but adjust to your capability. Perform one set of 12 to 15 repetitions.

CHEST PRESS

With a dumbbell in each hand at chest level, extend your arms toward the ceiling.

ASSESSMENT: Golf Posture/Alternate-Arm Reach (No. 9). On page 32.

ISOLATION CHEST PRESS

With a dumbbell in each hand, extend one arm vertically while keeping the other at your chest. Slowly alternate pressing both arms toward the ceiling.

ASSESSMENT: One-Leg Balance Straight-Arm Lift (No. 6). On page 31.

PULLOVERS

Using a single dumbbell in both hands behind your head and with your feet on the bench, extend your arms overhead and raise the weight until it's vertical. Be sure to keep your head back and your neck supported.

ASSESSMENT: Arms-Overhead Squat (No. 16). On page 36.

PULLOVER CRUNCH

Same as above but at the top of the movement, elevate your head and shoulders off the bench to isolate your abdominal muscles.

ASSESSMENT: Arms-Out Squat Rotation (No. 17). On page 36.

DUMBBELL ROW

Bend at the waist and place one hand on a bench or stability ball with your knees bent. Hold a single dumbbell at your side and lift toward your shoulder. Try to rotate your mid-back during the row for a little extra "pull." Be sure to focus on your posture and keeping your back flat.

ASSESSMENT: Behind-Your-Back Straight-Arm Lift (No. 7). On page 31.

HIP STRETCH

This is an example of how I put a functional stretch in between the weight-training exercises. Support yourself by holding onto a bar, cross one foot over the opposite knee, and lower yourself so that your thigh is parallel to the floor. If you struggle to maintain your posture, don't bend your leg all the way to 90 degrees; it's more important to focus on form. Perform three repetitions on each leg, holding each stretch for a breath.

For the next three exercises, start from a sitting position on a bench or stability ball. Perform one set of 12 to 15 repetitions with each leg or arm.

SINGLE-LEG BENCH SQUAT

With a manageable weight at your chest (remember, lighter is better to maintain form), extend one leg in front of you and stand on the other. Try to lower yourself back to the bench slowly but stand up as quickly as you can. If you struggle with this exercise, try keeping the heel of your elevated leg on the ground while you stand.
ASSESSMENT: Arms-Out Squat (No. 15). On page 35.

CURLS

With a dumbbell in each hand extended down by your sides and palms in, bend both elbows simultaneously while keeping them close to your side. Be sure to sit upright on the bench to eliminate poor posture. You can also perform this exercise by alternating curls with each arm.
ASSESSMENT: Toe Touch (No. 13). On page 34.

REVERSE CURLS

Same as above but with your palms out. Reverse curls isolate the muscles in your forearm and will likely require you use lighter dumbbells.

ASSESSMENT: Heel Touch (No. 14). On page 35.

The next three exercises are done standing up with a dumbbell in each hand. Perform one set of 12 to 15 repetitions.

EXTERNAL ROTATION

From your golf posture with your elbows at your side, bend your arms to a 90-degree angle and rotate the dumbbells away from you until you reach a maximum range or until your elbows separate from your side. This exercise replicates what your shoulders do in the golf swing and will likely require lighter weights.

ASSESSMENT: Club-Across-Chest One-Leg Rotation (No. 18). On page 37.

SIDE RAISES

Standing straight up with your arms at your side, extend your arms horizontally out to the side, being careful not to elevate past your shoulders.

ASSESSMENT: Behind-Your-Back Straight-Arm Lift/Rotate (No. 8). On page 32.

FRONT RAISES

Standing straight up with the dumbbells extended in front of your thighs, raise your arms horizontally in front of your shoulders.

ASSESSMENT: Straight-Arm Push/One-Arm Lift (No. 2). On page 29.

SWINGS

From your golf posture, hold one dumbbell with both hands and begin at your address position. Turn to the top of your backswing while maintaining your lower body position as you would in your golf swing. Focus on what you're trying to do with your golf swing and try to simulate that during this exercise; repeat on non-dominant side.

SUMMARY

If you want to add a power package to your workout, especially for your lower body, I recommend a similar plan to what Billy Horschel has done since his days playing at the University of Florida. After warming up, he does a deadlift where you start from a squatting position and raise the barbell to your thighs as you stand. He begins with eight reps at 90 pounds, then increases to five reps and 110 pounds, before finishing with three reps at 135.

Next, he does a power clean, which is similar to a deadlift except you snatch the bar up to your chest. He starts with eight reps at 75 pounds, then five reps at 90 pounds and three reps at 110. He finishes with a bar squat, starting with eight reps at 135 pounds, five reps at 155 and three reps at 175. He also does two upper-body power motions: the traditional bench press with eight reps at 135 pounds, five reps at 155, and three reps at 175, as well as seated front lat pulls with eight reps at 110 pounds, five reps at 125 and three reps at 140.

Before instituting any kind of heavy lifting, I highly recommend working with a certified trainer on your program and technique because you can get hurt if you don't know what you're doing. You want to make sure the value of this type of program is worth your time. You'll also want to rest the day after and do your assessments and/or correctives to maintain your flexibility.

BILLY HORSCHEL is a modern day golf athlete. The former FedEx Cup champion is diligent with his fitness routine. Billy (Billy Ho) has worked hard to improve his lower body strength and back flexibility. He is called "the stripe show" because of his laser like iron play.

CHAPTER NINE

SPEED

TRAINING WITH DIFFERENT-WEIGHT CLUBS

AFTER MORE THAN TWO DECADES training every level of player, I have discovered two proven generalizations when it comes to the differences between Tour-level golfers and recreational amateurs. The first is an elite player's better proprioception, which is essentially the ability to feel balance as Zach Johnson demonstrates in Chapter Six. The other distinction is the top-level player's ability to swing the club with speed from both the dominant (the right side for right-handed players) and non-dominant sides. Most recreational golfers can generate speed from their dominate side, but when I ask them to swing from the left or non-dominant side, it's usually pretty bad. Most Tour players, however, have the balance and coordination to create speed from their non-dominant side. A right-handed Tour player likely can't hit the ball 300-yards left-handed, but he can make contact and keep the ball in play. Most recreational golfers' non-dominant swings are robotic and mechanical; there's no "swoosh." It's become a fundamental part of any assessment I do when players arrive at Sea Island Resort. I even show them their non-dominant swings on video to show them their imbalance or lack of symmetry and consistency. By contrast, many high-level players contend their non-dominant swing actually looks more fundamentally sound than their dominant swing. Dustin Johnson used to tell me his action was better left-handed than it was right-handed. I would say 60 percent of the players on Tour have a decent left-handed swing.

Just as the goal of the mobility and stability chapters was to increase your club-head speed and hit the ball farther, the same objective applies to this chapter, but the difference is you'll be able to see improvement after just a few weeks of speed drills, which can help you increase your club-head speed by improving your sequencing efficiency by kind of tricking your body into resetting the pace of your motor pattern.

Many of my pros and I like SuperSpeed Golf's three-step system for "overspeed" training. You train by alternating clubs that are 20 percent lighter than a driver, 10 percent lighter and 5 percent heavier. Piggybacking on research from other sports such as track and baseball, the company conducted three years' worth of research on the right weighting structure and protocols for golf to get the best results. They found that if the club is too light, the body will not recreate the same motor pattern biomechanically and if it's too heavy, it'll train your body to swing slower. The company says players will typically gain up to eight percent more swing speed in the first 4-6 weeks, and all it requires is just three, 10-minute sessions a week. To increase difficulty, I also have my players repeat this program from their knees, which increases the amount of hip restriction.

You can also create speed in your golf swing by training with a medicine ball through a series of drills I helped develop with Nike Golf in 2010 alongside some of the game's top instructors, including Mike Bender and Sean Foley. Nike Sparq (Speed, Power, Agility, Reaction, and Quickness) was created as a power-testing model and includes three assessments: medicine-ball throw, medicine-ball bounce throw, and sit-up throw. Each drill includes three throws from both your dominant and non-dominant sides (except the sit-up, of course). In the assessment phase, you'll take the longest of the three throws and average them. For example, if your dominant throw is 30 feet and your non-dominant throw is 20 feet you will score an average of 25 feet for your baseline assessment. Your target score for each throw is 25 feet and you'll want to structure your workouts to focus on specific throws that need improvement, which for most recreational golfers will be their non-dominant throws. It will be necessary to have your trainer or workout partner assist you during this assessment phase, but after that you can use a wall or a rebounder board to perform the drills.

These speed exercises will help you maximize your distance—consider that an increase of 10 mph to your driver swing speed equates to an additional 25 yards off the tee—and you'll want to do them before you play, as well as during your workout routines.

STANDING

After going through your normal warm-up drills, you'll swing the lightest club as fast as possible three times from both your dominant and non-dominant side; repeat with medium- and heavy-weighted clubs.

KNEELING

SpeedGolf recommends doing the same drills again with a step in the same direction as you swing, but you can also do them on your knees from each side for even more of a challenge.

For the following three medicine-ball drills, begin with five reps and increase them as you become more comfortable.

MEDICINE-BALL THROW

From your golf posture, throw a six-pound medicine ball as hard as you can from the top of your backswing. Focus on maintaining your posture and balance just as you would during your swing. This is a connection test and challenges your total body. You can perform this exercise on one leg (trail leg) to create more of a challenge; switch sides.

MEDICINE-BALL BOUNCE

From your golf posture, bounce a six-pound medicine ball from the top of your backswing into the ground just in front of your forward foot—essentially where the golf ball would be. This drill challenges your upper body and lats; switch sides.

SIT-UP THROW

From a sit-up position with your arms extended over your head, throw a six-pound medicine ball as you perform a sit-up. This drill challenges your core.

HARRIS ENGLISH makes the golf swing look easy and effortless. Tall and lean, Harry puts his focus into all aspects of physical conditioning. Proper nutrition and mobility for his hips and back are critical for the two-time Tour winner. Look for this guy to blossom into a real superstar over the next few years.

CHAPTER TEN

NUTRITION

YOUR GLYCEMIC INDEX IS JUST AS IMPORTANT AS YOUR HANDICAP INDEX

WHEN A TOUR PROFESSIONAL lands in his private jet the Monday or Tuesday of tournament week, the first stop he makes in his courtesy car isn't at the course, the gym, or some fancy restaurant. It's at Whole Foods to get his food supply for the week. That's how relevant good nutrition has become on Tour. A lot of guys will get their protein source through nuts because they're easily digestible, so they're buying almonds and cashews. They'll buy protein bars and cereal, which won't have any sugar, and almond or coconut milk. They're buying wholegrain bread and coconut or almond butter. They'll also go back to Whole Foods during the week for dinner. They love it. It's become the new 19th hole on Tour. The first time I went to a Champions Tour event in 1989, it was Snickers bars and Cokes and vodkas and beers. Now, players are demanding to have the proper nutrition every week.

If you want to play better, not to mention increase your chances of living a longer, healthier life, you should, too. If you're going to change your body, you've got to change your eating habits. Evaluating your nutritional intake is crucial if you want to maintain your energy on the course. You need to do what the Tour players do and that includes doing a food allergy test, which my players do every other year because those things can change. It's a lot like doing a club fitting. Everyone is different, so you need an individualized plan just like you need custom specs for your clubs. Lee Trevino actually turned me onto it in the mid-1990s. He struggled with his weight his whole life and found out he had a food allergy to yeast, so he eliminated yeast and dairy products from his diet and lost a good deal of weight and a lot of his arthritic issues.

Davis' and Randy's Ryder Cup Shake

1 Cup of almond milk or coconut water

1 Tablespoon of almond butter

4 Strawberries

1 Banana

1 Dozen blueberries

1 Teaspoon of honey

½ Cup of granola

1 Cup of ice

How many times have you played a terrific 12 or 14 holes, only to peter out at the end, and lose focus and shots? Chances are it wasn't your Handicap Index that did you in but your glycemic index—the effect of carbs on your blood sugar levels. But if you do it right, you should have as much energy coming up 18 as you did walking down 1. Although I highly recommend adding a nutritionist to your team, here are some basic nutritional guidelines that will really help you the next time you play.

Want to start your day off right before even getting to the course? After waking up, skip the coffee and drink two glasses of water. Next, get in a 15-minute workout by doing the assessment routine from Chapter Two and some of the balance and tubing exercises from Chapter Six. For breakfast, eat a wholegrain cereal with fruit or an egg or two with some wholegrain toast. If you prefer to stop at Starbucks on your way to the course, skip the muffin and get the oatmeal with fruit with little or no brown sugar.

Hydration is key toward stabilizing your hunger and energy levels, so be sure to include a good water bottle like a Hydro Flask or Yeti in your bag that you can refill during the round. You might think you're hungry when you're actually thirsty. After your warm-up on the range, drink two glasses of water. Skip the sugary sports drink because it destabilizes your blood sugar and can actually make you more tired in the long run. Instead, add a supplement like one from Nuun, an effervescent tablet that's an electro-lyte replacement with no sugar. There are four essential electrolytes—calcium, mag-nesium, potassium, and sodium—and the amount you need depends on the ambient temperature. You need more if it's hot or cold to help regulate your body temperature. If you have to drink a sports drink, here's how to avoid downing all those sugars at once: drink a third of it, then fill it with water, drink half, and then fill it with water again.

During your round, continue to sip water and avoid the cart girl and halfway house. Both are full of food hazards, like cheese crackers, energy bars, burgers, and hot dogs. Look for fruit and nuts or a better yet carry your own bag of unsalted almonds and cashews, beef or turkey jerky, or an almond-butter sandwich on wholegrain. Not only will you save money, but you'll also be storing energy for the back nine. Also, don't ride every step of the way; alternate walking holes with your cart partner to keep your hips and back loose.

If you follow these tips, chances are you won't be famished at lunch and overeat. A simple tuna sandwich on wholegrain with light mayo should do. Why wholegrain bread? Because white flour has no fiber and all the vitamins and minerals have been stripped away. These simple carbs quickly release sugars into the bloodstream and can add inches to your waistline.

While the above tips can definitely improve your golf scores, this one can improve your vital signs: choose fish or seafood, like shrimp, over chicken, beef, or pork whenever possible. Meat, even chicken, has omega-6 fats and oils that cause inflammation, which is responsible for any number of maladies, especially as we age. Fish and seafood have omega-3 fats and oils that are actually anti-inflammatory. They're not only great for your joints but your brain and memory, too, and might just help you to think your way around the course better.

CHAPTER ELEVEN

SENIORS

AN AGE-DEFYING BLUEPRINT

W HEN TIGER WOODS finally returned to tournament golf at his own Hero World Challenge in The Bahamas in December of 2016 after almost a year and a half away, he played in the pro-am with retired New York Yankee great Derek Jeter. He asked "Jetes" how long it took him to get ready for each game as he got older. Jeter's answer, "Three to four hours."

"It's the same thing for me," Tiger said. "I was in the gym with Rosie (Justin Rose), and he's in there doing the same thing. He's 36 now, and it takes him an hour, hour and a half, just to be able to go and hit balls. You have to activate the muscles."

If world-class athletes like Woods, Jeter, and Rose take more than an hour to get ready to play, where does that leave a senior player? Sure, you can hop out of your car, warm-up by hitting a few balls on the range before teeing off, and maybe play half decently, or maybe not. Wouldn't it be nice if it weren't such a crapshoot? As I've said over and over again, you need to properly prepare your body to play consistent golf, particularly if you're dealing with any injuries, and I don't know many seniors who don't have at least one or two nagging areas.

Take Jim Stahl, for example. I first met the top amateur in the early 2000s when he came to me to help get his game back. After a lifetime of playing golf at an impressively high level, his body had betrayed him. When I asked him to balance on his left leg, his bad leg, he tumbled into a mirror. He's big and strong and a really good athlete, but golf had taken its toll on his body. I was shocked by his lack of flexibility and balance for such

When I first met **GARY PLAYER** early in my career, two things immediately impressed me: his enthusiasm and desire to improve. Known as the father of golf fitness, I was shocked that he was interested in learning what I thought about his functional movement and ability to get better. To this day, I credit the time I spent with Gary as a big part of the foundation for my career. His swing is still effortless and powerful. Gary is super committed to promoting longevity and bringing worldwide awareness to good health and nutrition. Every year at the Masters, I make sure to watch him hit the ceremonial drive Thursday morning. You're the best Mr. Player!

a good player. Like so many from his generation, Jim had learned the game as a caddie. He grew up in Cincinnati and was a frequent competitor of Jack Nicklaus when the two were juniors. He went on to become a successful businessman and had an impressive amateur career, highlighted by his victory at the 1995 U.S. Senior Amateur, before successive back surgeries in 1999, 2001, and 2014 left him frustrated and feeling as if his best days on the course were behind him.

That's not to say Jim gave up. A member of Seminole Golf Club in south Florida, Ocean Forest on Sea Island, and the R&A, he didn't go gently into that good golf night, but his search for a trainer who could reverse the effects of three back surgeries proved challenging. Jim kindly credits me with helping him get his body and game back thanks to a program I designed for him to reverse the impact of multiple back surgeries. He now maintains a two handicap and plays three times a week.

Although his story is certainly inspiring, it's hardly unique. In fact, my Masters' thesis explored the impacts of aging on the golf swing. When you're dealing with senior golfers who have had hip replacements, knee replacements, and back injuries, generally what happens is the opportunity to re-injure themselves playing golf is greater, so the number one goal for us is injury prevention for more longevity. In Jim's case, it was a dramatic loss of mobility that had made a lifetime love affair with golf go sour, but it's a common challenge for players as they age whether they've been impacted by injuries or not. It's also why I consider senior golfers my most rewarding clients because they're the easiest with which to see improvements. In most cases, it's all mobility based and that's an area you can focus on and improve. With most seniors, poor play is more often than not the byproduct of an injury, which has created compensations in a swing, not the other way around. If I get a player like Jim who's already had some injuries, we'll do some rehabilitation work to get him to swing the way he used to. The motor patterns that existed for 30 or 40 years can be altered quickly when someone gets injured.

Recovering from these injuries and reversing the impact they have had on a golf swing often depends on how quickly and diligently a player begins a targeted fitness program like the one outlined in this chapter and demonstrated by Jim. The biggest thing is to get them to regain their range of motion. Injured players become protective in their golf swings and lose explosiveness and distance. It's a battle to get them to swing the way they used to, but it's a battle that can be won. Your weapon is a specific and proven blueprint that I perfected after more than two decades of trial and error, and it can work for you just like it did for Jim.

For the following eight drills, begin in your golf posture with a stability ball against the wall. Start with five repetitions and increase them as you become more comfortable.

WALL PUSH

With the ball at waist height, push up the wall as high as you can with both hands. Focus on stretching both arms and shoulders equally, which will allow you to identify areas that may be tight or restricted. Shoulder issues, for example, will cause your arms to bend during this motion.

PELVIC TILT

With the ball at chest height, push your hips in and out. This will activate your core and stretch your hips as well as identify any restrictions. Hip issues will make your abdomen feel unstable. You should feel a stretch in your lower back and tightness in your core during this exercise.

ISOLATION KNEE LIFT

With the ball at head height, "march" in place, alternately lifting both legs until your thighs are parallel to the ground. Be sure that each leg can be elevated equally and that you have enough stability and balance to keep from drifting to either side.

ONE-ARM LIFT

While holding the ball as high as possible with one arm, slowly raise the other arm above your shoulder trying to create as much stretch as you can. Focus on keeping your arm on the same plain as your shoulder with your elbow straight; switch arms.

LATERAL-TORSO ROTATION

With the wall to your side, hold the ball at shoulder height with the arm closest to the wall. Slowly reach your opposite arm across your chest and try to touch the wall, creating a turn similar to your golf swing. Focus on maintaining your spine angle as you reach across.

WALL SQUAT/ONE-ARM PULL

With the ball wedged between the wall and your lower back, do a half-squat and slowly pull your left arm across your chest with your right hand. Be sure that your left arm remains straight and hold each "pull" for three breaths; switch arms.

ASSISTED-WALL SQUAT

With the ball wedged between the wall and your lower back, sit down as far as you can but don't let your thighs get lower than parallel to the floor.

BACKSWING ROTATION ASSISTANCE

With the ball wedged between your lower back and the wall, do a half-squat and have
your trainer or workout partner help you turn your shoulders into a backswing and
hold the position to create more range of motion. The goal is to complete the squat
and then make the turn, but initially you're trying to assure the squat is correct before
completing the rotation.

MORGAN PRESSEL was a special athlete before she became a teenager. Her flexibility and balance were what stood out when her coach came to see me for an evaluation. When she was younger, she took dance and ballet classes. I believe these activities helped shape her golf swing in many ways. We primarily focused on getting stronger and developing her core and lower body stability. Like many young golfers, our goal was to teach her a system that would benefit her long-term. Morgan quickly adapted and became an excellent golfer with a repeatable swing.

CHAPTER TWELVE

WOMEN AND JUNIORS

BALANCING GOOD FLEXIBILITY
WITH BETTER STABILITY

IN CHAPTER TWO, the assessment chapter, I mentioned that there's only been about a dozen players who passed all 18 evaluations on their first attempt. One of those was Morgan Pressel, who was just 14 at the time. That's when her grandfather, Herb Krickstein, first brought her to PGA National, driving her from Boca Raton to Palm Beach Gardens two times a week to work with me. She was one of the top juniors in the country and had recently become the youngest player to qualify for the U.S. Women's Open at age 12 in 2001 (Lexi Thompson beat her by a few months in 2007, and Thompson was later surpassed by Lucy Li in 2014).

One day, Herb and I were having a conversation about all the colleges offering scholarships and I told him, "She won't be going to college. She's going to win on the LPGA Tour before then." He just shot me a look like, What? I said, "She moves better than any athlete in her sport now. Her consistency with her body and how it moves is on an elite level and better than any LPGA player I've seen, many of whom had won." Three years later at 17, she was tied for the lead on the 72nd hole in the 2005 U.S. Women's Open at Cherry Hills near Denver but lost by a stroke when Birdie Kim holed out from a greenside bunker in the group ahead of her. Later that summer, she won the U.S. Women's Amateur before turning pro that fall. Two years after that at age 19, she won the Kraft

Nabisco Championship, becoming the youngest winner ever of a modern LPGA major at the time (Lydia Ko eclipsed her at the 2015 Evian Championship).

While her flexibility and mobility were incredibly dynamic, the one thing she lacked was strength, which is typical of most women and juniors. She needed to gain some size to gain some distance, so we did a fair amount of weight training like you see in Chapters Seven and Eight. A typical junior or woman can pass 70 percent of my assessment tests, while a typical man can only pass about 30 percent. Juniors and women are usually more symmetrical, too, so weight training can be more beneficial for both, particularly for the wrists, forearms and shoulders. They don't have to worry about getting hurt as much as men.

One of the top juniors I work with at Sea Island when he's here with his family is Will Thomson, who, like Morgan, is a once-in-a-generation player from a physical perspective. In 2014, he became the youngest person ever to qualify for the U.S. Amateur at age 13 and, as *Golfweek's* No. 1-ranked recruit in the class of 2019, he has already committed to playing for the University of Texas. He was 11 when Todd Anderson and I first developed a detailed plan integrating the technical swing aspects with a training program that his team at home monitors and implements.

Thomson is hardly an outlier when it comes to the cutting edge of instruction and fitness, with the top juniors increasingly conditioned to think in holistic terms. What were once considered advanced training programs developed for the game's top players are now crucial parts of any junior's development. But the challenges of working with juniors are entirely different to those faced by a weekend golfer, or even a Tour player for that matter. The biggest thing is not understanding where they are flexible or need to be flexible when they are younger, so when they age and put on body mass, they don't lose range of motion and their swing. What we're trying to do is hit on all the benchmarks of flexibility that all the Tour players have and then sustain them through the growth pattern.

Before the development of comprehensive fitness programs for juniors, a player would go through a normal "growth spurt" and often struggle with their swing as their body changes. Some of the benchmarks we've established with the juniors are more high-tech than others thanks to the introduction of 3D motion capture, but most are as basic as a physical assessment.

I want to see extensive flexibility with juniors. It gives us a foundation for building strength without having any limitations. In the case of an athlete like Will, who played other sports, we're looking to see if the hamstrings and hips are flexible. How's the lower back and shoulders? In his case, he was excellent across the board. After an initial focus on flexibility and lateral movement, which included about 15 to 20 minutes of stretching and dynamic movement two to three days a week like the junior in this chapter

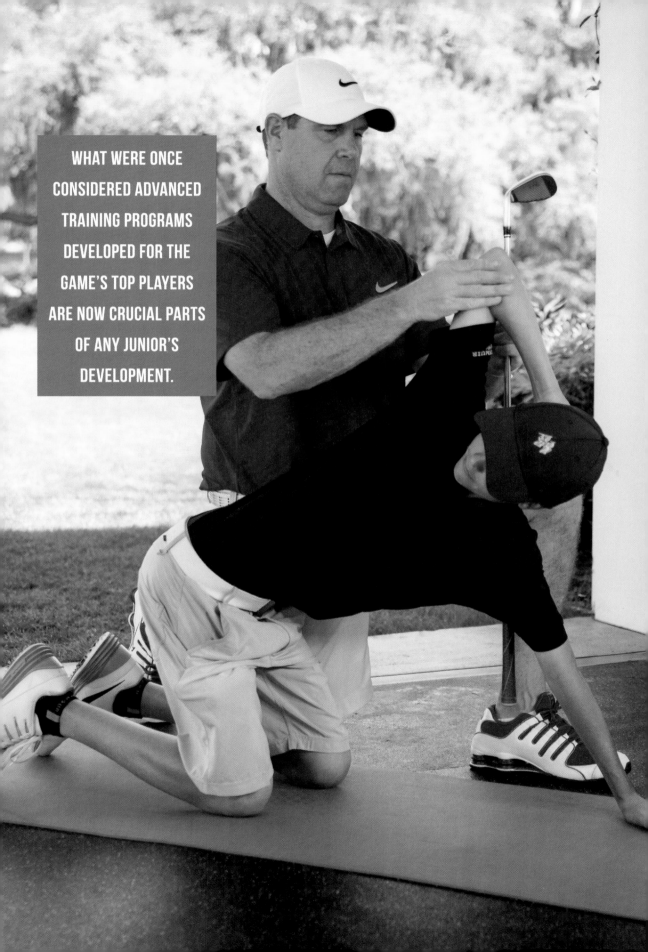

WHAT WERE ONCE CONSIDERED ADVANCED TRAINING PROGRAMS DEVELOPED FOR THE GAME'S TOP PLAYERS ARE NOW CRUCIAL PARTS OF ANY JUNIOR'S DEVELOPMENT.

USGA President Diana Murphy has been a client of mine since I started working at Sea Island over ten years ago. Along with her husband Reg, I have helped them with a workout program for maintaining their golf fitness. She is a good golfer, who drives the ball straight and long.

demonstrates, the intensity and focus shifted as he matured into light-weight training before eventually moving into a Tour-type fitness program now. It's crucial for Will and other juniors to adhere to this progression due to the unique challenges of a body that is changing so dramatically in such a short period of time.

Most people would think a program for a junior would include heavy lifting, but it really is more a function of mobility and movement and less about strength training, at least at first. Strength training comes along as their body goes through puberty and they get a little more mature. Although a junior's commitment to a fitness plan is crucial, I also focus on getting a player's parents involved in any program in an effort to create accountability. It's vital to include them in the process. A small amount of fitness will benefit the junior tremendously, but including the parent allows the child to work toward a goal in overall health.

We live in the "praise generation" where every parent thinks his or her child is going to be the next Jordan Spieth. Few are, of course, but the greatest gift a parent can give his son or daughter is a lifelong ability to get the most out of their game and an introduction to a lifestyle of physical conditioning. Regardless where their career in golf takes them, a golf fitness plan will give them a foundation for a lifetime of good health, injury avoidance and positive self-image, not to mention a better golf game.

For all the routines that follow, do each one eight times, holding the last stretch for three breaths. I also recommend doing the assessment addition 10 times after each exercise.

KNEELING-HIP FLEXOR

This is one of the best assessment drills for juniors because it allows us to check for tightness in their hips, quads, and torso. From a kneeling position with one leg extended, push your front knee forward until you feel a stretch through your quadriceps (the front of your thighs). Add a back stretch to this motion by holding a club in front of you and rotating during the stretch toward the leg that is forward; switch legs. **ASSESSMENT:** Arms-Out Squat (No. 15) on page 35.

SEATED ROTATION

This stretch will assess hamstring and hip mobility. Sit with your feet driver-width apart and extend a club in front of you at shoulder height. Rotate your arms in both directions and try to keep your legs straight and your toes pointed vertically. **ASSESSMENT:** Arms-Out Squat Rotation (No. 17) on page 36.

BRIDGE

This stretch will assess glute strength and hip mobility. Lying on your back with your knees bent, feet flat, and your arms extended in front of you, push your hips up. Try to keep your feet and knees aligned and square with your body.

ASSESSMENT: Straight-Arm Lunge Rotation (No. 12) on page 34.

ONE-LEG-EXTENDED BRIDGE

This stretch will assess glute stability and hamstring tightness. Lying on your back with your knees bent, feet flat, and your arms extended in front of you, push your hips up and then extend one leg vertically. Try to extend your leg as straight as possible with your heel aligned with your hip and your foot parallel to the ceiling; switch legs.

ASSESSMENT: Club-Across-Chest One-Leg Rotation (No. 18) on page 37.

ALTERNATE ARM/LEG LIFT

This stretch will assess the symmetry of your mobility between your shoulders and hips. Lying on your stomach, lift your right arm in front of you to shoulder height and your left leg as high as you can. Try to lift both your leg and arm the same height; switch sides.

ASSESSMENT: One-Leg Balance Straight-Arm Lift (No. 6) on page 31.

FOREARM PLANK

There are many variations of a basic plank motion, but this stretch will allow a junior to assess his or her core stability. Lying on your stomach with your feet shoulder-width apart, bring your elbows under your shoulders and push your hips up eight times, holding each stretch for a breath.

ASSESSMENT: Arms Overhead-Horizontal Reach (No. 4) on page 30.

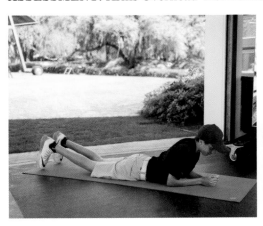 

J.T. POSTON has had an incredible run to the Tour. Just out of college, this young gun went from no status to his rookie year in less than six months. He's tall and thin, so building muscle mass is important to his longevity. A hard worker in the fitness room, he has already seen improvement with better lower body stability and abdominal strength.

CHAPTER THIRTEEN

PRE-GOLF

WHAT TO KNOW BEFORE YOU GO

"GIVE ME SOME THINGS I CAN DO AT THE COURSE BEFORE I PLAY." The request has become so ubiquitous I long ago created a pre-golf stretching program that has changed little throughout the years and become a staple for all of my students regardless of skill level. People are so pressed for time these days that they rarely arrive at the course having done any kind of warm-up, but hopefully, now that you've read my book, you'll at least go through the assessments before leaving the house or your club's fitness center. But I realize that's not always possible, so here are some things you can do to prepare your body at the course.

This pre-golf program should take less than 10 minutes to complete and begins in the locker room and continues on the range, working from your lower body to your upper body. Although this is a fraction of the time a Tour player dedicates to his pre-round or pre-practice stretching, which normally takes about 30 minutes, for most recreational golfers that's not an option. But the worst thing you can do is swing a club without any dynamic stretching! A pre-golf warm-up will give you your best chance to play well and, perhaps more importantly, help reduce the chance of injury by loosening up your golf muscles.

Chances are you'll be paying a visit the locker room beforehand, so let's start there. Hold each stretch for two breaths and repeat three times with each leg.

SEATED HIP/GLUTE STRETCH

After sitting down to put on your golf shoes, cross your left leg over your right knee and push down on your left knee to create a stretch in your hip and glute; switch legs.

HAMSTRING/LOWER-BACK STRETCH

Place your left leg on a chair in front of you, bend at the waist, and try to touch your toes with your right hand; switch legs.

ROTATION STRETCH

With both hands across your chest, rotate your shoulders 90 degrees keeping your head down. Reach to your side with both arms keeping them parallel to each other.

Out on the range before you start hitting balls, do each of the three warm-ups below three times each, holding each stretch for two breaths.

TORSO

From your golf posture, extend a club in front of you and rotate your body into your backswing and follow-through. Try to turn each shoulder down to your golf ball or the center of your stance.

HIPS AND CHEST

From your golf posture, hold a club across your chest and make a complete turn in both directions. Try to point the club at your opposite foot: left shoulder at the right foot in the backswing (for right-handed players), right shoulder at left foot in the follow-through.

TRICEPS

From your golf posture, hold a club overhead. Slowly move one arm down behind your back and pull on the club to stretch your opposite shoulders and triceps; switch arms.

In 1998, I wrote an instructional article for Golf Digest outlining the importance of maintaining flexibility during a round of golf and how a player could use a golf cart to perform simple stretches, similar to the next chapter in this book. After reading the article, Hugh Reilly, a PGA of America club professional from Pennsylvania, sent me a message: "Stretching is great, but I like to walk."

With my input, Hugh created the first version of the Stretching Pole for players, like him who didn't have access to a golf cart during a round but still wanted to remain flexible. The Stretching Pole complies with the Rules of Golf, so you can carry it in your golf bag and actually use during the round to stay limber while you play like many of the world's best players, including Dustin Johnson, Rickie Fowler, and Davis Love III.

Repeat each stretch three times, holding each one for two breaths.

UPPER BODY

From your golf posture, hold the Stretching Pole in front of you on a slight angle and push your head down through your arms. Make sure your feet are square to the pole as you push your hips back during each stretch.

BACKSWING STRETCH

From your golf posture with the Stretching Pole in front of you and to the right (for right-handed players), hold the top of the pole and rotate to the top of your backswing. Try to point your left shoulder to your right foot.

FOLLOW-THROUGH STRETCH

From your golf posture holding the handle of the Stretching Pole front of you and the end behind your left heel (for right-handed players), rotate to the top of your follow-through. Try to point your right shoulder over your left foot.

A PRE-GOLF WARM-UP WILL GIVE YOU YOUR BEST CHANCE TO PLAY WELL AND, PERHAPS MORE IMPORTANTLY, HELP REDUCE THE CHANCE OF INJURY BY LOOSENING UP YOUR GOLF MUSCLES.

BRANDT SNEDEKER has been a big time winner on the PGA Tour. He owns eight career victories along with a FedEx Cup trophy. A great putter and short game wizard, "Sneds" has overcome two hip surgeries and puts time into keeping his body explosive and strong.

CHAPTER FOURTEEN

GOLF CART

MID-ROUND DO'S AND DON'TS

WHILE I HIGHLY RECOMMEND walking over riding to stay fit and loose, I realize that's not always possible. The good news for riders is that the golf cart, with all its handles and supports, is really well suited to helping you stay limber during the round, particularly those areas you feel are tight. Golf is a hurry-up-and-wait sport, so it's important to keep stretching whenever you find yourself standing around waiting to hit. For even the quickest players, an 18-hole round of golf takes just under four hours. During that time the muscles that you activated in your pre-golf warm-up will become tight and fatigued, which is why you need stretches you can do while you play.

The goal would be to perform each of these stretches at least once or twice throughout your round to loosen up tight areas, which typically is the shoulders and arms early in the round. As you play, however, it's your legs and back that normally become tired and tight so you'll want to focus on those areas as your round progresses.

All of these stretches are "holding" drills so you'll want to pause for two breaths during each repetition. If you feel tight in a particular area, repeat the stretch; otherwise you can move on to the next drill.

SHOULDERS AND MID-BACK

Stand about three feet from the golf cart with your hands on the roof and your feet shoulder-width apart. Push your head down between your shoulders as you push your hips back.

CHEST AND SHOULDERS

Stand with your shoulders at a 90-degree angle to the cart, reach back with one arm and grab the front support bar. With your arm extended away from your body, slowly turn your torso away from your hand; switch sides.

MID-BACK ROTATION

Same as before but grab the front support bar with both arms extended. Lower your head between your shoulders, trying to align your shoulders with a spot directly between your feet; switch sides.

HIP AND GLUTE

Stand facing the cart with both hands on the front support bar and cross your right foot over your left knee. Sit back by slowly bending your left knee until your left thigh is parallel to the ground; switch legs.

HAMSTRINGS

Stand facing the cart and place one foot just behind the seat and slowly bend forward and grab the canopy handle. Keep your leg straight, but not locked; switch legs.

THE GOAL WOULD BE TO PERFORM EACH OF THESE STRETCHES AT LEAST ONCE OR TWICE THROUGHOUT YOUR ROUND TO LOOSEN UP TIGHT AREAS, WHICH TYPICALLY IS THE SHOULDERS AND ARMS EARLY IN THE ROUND.

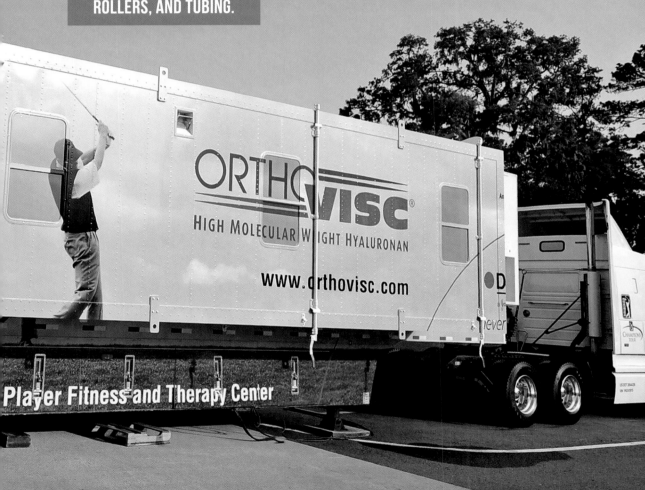

THE FITNESS TRAILER HAS ALMOST EVERYTHING WE NEED WITH TREADMILLS, BIKES, ELLIPTICALS, CABLE-CROSS MACHINE, DUMBBELLS, STABILITY BALLS, FOAM ROLLERS, AND TUBING.

CHAPTER FIFTEEN

OUT ON TOUR

WORKING COHESIVELY TO
KEEP THE PROFESSIONAL PLAYERS FIT

M Y HOME AWAY FROM HOME when I'm out on Tour is the fitness trailer, which is actually two trailers these days. Each is 60 feet long, 16-feet wide, and 14-feet high (when parked) with one devoted to training, while the other is used for therapy sessions. There are also two sets of them, with one based on the West Coast and the other on the East Coast, serving both the PGA Tour and the Champions Tour. Professional drivers fly in Sunday morning and drive them to the next Tour stop and then fly home. It's really a well-coordinated effort, although there are some tour stops they don't go to, like Hawaii, of course. The trailers are open from Tuesday morning until the last time tee time on Sunday and are fully staffed with chiropractors, trainers, therapists, and nutritionists. There's a morning shift and afternoon shift of six to eight guys. I have great relationships with the other trainers. We work very cohesively.

The fitness trailer has almost everything we need with treadmills, bikes, ellipticals, cable-cross machine, dumbbells, stability balls, foam rollers, and tubing. There's even a shelf loaded with Nike workout clothes and sneakers right inside the door for players to change into from their "golf costume," as Davis Love III says. The equipment has really been upgraded and is a lot more golf-specific, whereas historically it was just some bikes, treadmills, and a Universal strength machine. Years ago, players would stick a six-pack in the fridge and just ride the bike till the beer was cold, but it's much busier these days as players have become more cognizant that a better body means better golf. There's usually a Tuesday morning rush because players want to get their week off on a good start. Wednesday is also pretty busy with workouts, but then it's mostly warmups the rest of the week when the tournament rounds get under way. At majors, the cream really rises to the top, so it's not uncommon to see the top 30 players in the world in there a couple times

Luke Guthrie doing a split-stance one arm pull.

a day. Rookies aren't even sure if they're even able to use it, so it's not uncommon for me to introduce them to it, which is good because a player wants to establish a good fitness routine as early as possible in his career.

The atmosphere is pretty relaxed with a couple of TVs in each trailer that are always tuned to sports, baseball in the spring, football in the fall. The Australians love to watch any type of racing, whether it's autos, motorcycles, or go-carts, while the Euros are constantly fixed on soccer.

Below are some of the pros I work with and I describe one of the many routines they like to do inside the trailer during a Tour event.

Luke Guthrie has been successful at every level, but when he got on the PGA Tour three years ago, he realized he needed to be more engaged in his training program. Here he demonstrates a split-stance one-arm pull that helps fire-up his lats and shoulders. Although this is more of a strength-based movement, he would do this prior to playing, but with a lighter weight and more speed. He's a very symmetrical athlete and this drill allows him to engage his upper body, while stabilizing his lower body, similar to what a good player does during his backswing.

Billy Horschel is doing a kneeling one-arm horizontal reach, which he would do as a warmup drill prior to playing. Billy has a very comprehensive warmup program he's used throughout his professional career. We refine it in the off-season and then stick with it throughout the course of the season. It's very orchestrated and geared toward what he's working on his golf swing with coach Todd Anderson. This mobility drill is a good one because he's trying to keep his spine centered. His lower body is

Billy Horschel doing a kneeling one-arm horizontal reach.

Justin Leonard doing an alternating shoulder press.

stable, his right knee is on the ground, and he's got the stability ball against his other knee to make sure it doesn't move left as he reaches back with one arm. He's trying to really extend his chest and stay tall.

Justin Leonard is doing an alternating shoulder press on a stability ball. Justin is a real outdoors guy, skier, and cross-trainer who's very focused on fitness. He once ran a marathon in under four hours. The weight training he does is more about longevity than power. For the shoulder press, he likes a seated position to stabilize his hips while extending the dumbbells overhead, trying to push up as far as he can. Because he's alternating them, he's trying to get a feel for the shoulder and the lat pressing overhead while staying in a really upright spine position. His hips and core are engaged and then he's exploding up with the weight.

I started working with Kyle Reifers over 10 years ago when he was the No. 1 ranked amateur in the world at Wake Forest. Part of the reason he's so good is that he's able to rotate extremely well in both directions. For a taller player, getting on your knees and turning your shoulders to find out your range of motion in both directions is very important. This is a great exercise prior to playing or just in your general workout. Try to turn each shoulder over the opposite knee and hold for 10 seconds or a couple of breaths.

Michael Thompson is demonstrating a split-stance overhead lunge. I started working with him four years ago and he's the epitome of the muscular body type, but flexibility is key, so what he's trying to do here is increase the arc in his mid-back and shoulders while stabiliz-

Kyle Reifers checks his range of motion.

Michael Thompson doing a split-stance overhead lunge.

ing his lower body. This is a drill a Tour player will do multiple times a day before and after he plays. With the band attached at head level, he's trying to reach those arms as high as he can to create as much range of motion in his middle back. He'll hold it for a few breaths and then alternate legs to feel that stretch all the way from his hips through the mid-spine. It's a pretty impressive motion.

No, Charles Howell III isn't playing a giant game of Cat's Cradle. He's using tubing to focus on maximizing his range of motion with his turn while keeping that resistance band overhead—just like the connection in the golf swing, which goes from the legs to the torso and shoulders and then to the hands. It's a great assessment drill because recreational golfers who try this would probably struggle with keeping those arms overhead due to a lack of shoulder mobility.

Here Harold Varner III is doing a pretty impressive move with his Stretching Pole. The first time I met Harold at East Carolina University, I took him through the assessments from Chapter Two and he passed every one. He's one of those guys. Not surprisingly, he just won his first professional tournament at the Australian PGA last December, becoming the first American to win it since Hale Irwin in 1978. He's an incredibly freak athlete with both strength and speed. In order to have speed, you've got to make a really good turn and complete your backswing and as you can see with the Stretching Pole, he's able to rotate that left shoulder over his right knee.

The lateral lunge is a staple drill for Zach Johnson. He'll step side-to-side and really

Charles Howell III using tubing to focus on his range of motion.

Harold Varner III stretches with the Stretching Pole.

stretch through the abductors and hips while maintaining good posture. He does it with some speed and tempo, but the most important part is to feel how the ground and the legs work collectively together. It's a great warmup drill that a high percentage of Tour players do every day. Most recreational golfers just aren't warmed up enough with their lower body and it takes them a while to find out just how much lower-body speed they can generate. Tour players don't have that luxury.

The fitness trailer sure has come a long way since its first year on Tour in 1984. Prior to its arrival, "conditioning" was something players only did in the shower after shampooing. Dean Beman was the commissioner then of the PGA Tour and he was an early proponent of working out. In fact, when he was on Tour in the 1960s, he was one of the few guys on Tour who did, carrying a set of dumbbells from stop to stop. Of course, not everyone believed in it, like Lee Trevino.

"Look," he said during a tournament telecast in 1985, "this whole thing with the fitness trailer is just a fad. It won't last because golfers don't need muscles. Muscles can hurt a golfer. They can do all the lifting they want, but it won't help them score better. Golfers are born, not made. And another thing, by the time I practice, play, and practice some more, I don't want to exercise. I want a beer."

Ironically, I worked with Lee in the mid-1990s and he and changed his tune by then. Following neck surgery, he became a rehab junkie and bought into a comprehensive workout plan that included cardio and a light lifting program.

Zach Johnson doing a lateral lunge.

CHAPTER SIXTEEN

A FINAL WORD

BECOME FIT IN YOUR SPARE TIME

WITH MY TOUR PROS, many times we can't get in a full workout due to other obligations, such as with the media, sponsors, or fans, so we have to be able to adapt and adjust. Often times it's what can we do in a 15-minute window? A 5:00 o'clock workout that was going to last 45 minutes suddenly starts at 6:00 and has to be done by 6:15, so we might just do some mobility drills with the medicine ball to get their muscles activated in three planes of motion, along with some stretching and movement from the assessments and correctives. We're interested in an overall check: how are they moving, how are they squatting, how are their shoulders feeling? We'll correct anything that's not perfect before doing some flexibility. Even with the most highly conditioned players, we're correcting on a daily basis because their mobility can change from day to day based on how many balls they hit, what time they tee off, how they slept—all kinds of factors. In the old days, guys would sleep to 11:00 if they had a late tee time. Today, it's not uncommon for Tour pros to get in a full workout in the morning if they play later. When he has an afternoon tee time, Dustin Johnson likes to train for about an hour and a half around 8:30, then eat breakfast, shower, and get ready. With his super flexible body, he can actually lift weights before a round, but it would be more speed based with less weight and less reps.

IT MEANS A LOT ME TO SEE PEOPLE ENJOYING THEMSELVES ON THE COURSE BECAUSE THEIR BODIES ARE ALLOWING THEM TO PLAY BETTER.

Based upon your knowledge from this book, you should be able to take the five to eight exercises you need the most and do them in your spare time, whether that's at the office or at home for a few minutes at a time. Don't say I don't have time. Simply adjust by dummying down the program and doing a few things. If you've got more time on another day, then you can even do more exercises above what you normally do in your full routine, but the whole gym mentality where you can only improve if you pay for a gym membership, put on workout clothes, and motivate yourself to get to the gym is a thing of the past. Make my program fit your schedule, not the other way around.

Golf to me is about getting your body moving and being outside around nature. I love to see people enjoying the beauty of the activity. Studies have shown that you can live a longer life just by playing golf. It means a lot to me to see people enjoying themselves on the course because their bodies are allowing them to play better. When I get out of bed every day, it's about helping people get more motivated to perfect certain physical fitness skills that will allow them to play better and feel better about themselves and their games.

I feel very blessed to have a career where you can positively influence people on a daily basis. It's not a job. I love helping people achieve their goals. I started in a career that didn't exist 25 years ago. Private trainers used to be just for celebrities but not anymore and golf has a lot to do with the growth of personal training because golfers understood the value of instruction and the teachers knew the value of having their students work with certified trainers. In fact, one of the benchmarks for a trainer today is to be certified through the Titleist Performance Institute to work with golfers. It's truly humbling to have been there at the beginning and now see the amount of interest that exists from people of all ability levels to invest their time and energy into getting better. The opportunity to improve is there regardless of your age.

Clearly you're serious about your golf game or you wouldn't have purchased this book. Now's the time to get serious about your fitness plan if you want to become the best golfer you can be. I promise you, a better body will lead to better golf. Good luck, and come see me at Sea Island some time.

SEA ISLAND RESORT

ST. SIMONS ISLAND, GEORGIA

THERE ARE MANY GOOD REASONS to pay a visit to Sea Island—the five-star accommodations and dining at The Cloister and The Lodge, the three strategic and scenic Low Country courses, and the plethora of non-golf activities like fishing, tennis and water sports. But if you're serious about improving your game—whether it's the long game, short game, putting, or even fitness and the mental side—Sea Island is the place to come. It's like the Mayo Clinic for your ailing swing.

Located just north of Jacksonville on St. Simons Island, Ga., Sea Island Resort has

The Sea Island Performance Center offers custom club fitting.

always had one of the best instructional facilities in the country, but it's even better now after a recent upgrade to its Golf Performance Center (the resort also opened new, relaxed accommodations at The Inn). Overlooking the Intracoastal Waterway, the range at Sea Island has always had the best views of any practice area in the U.S., but with the new indoor putting lab, five covered hitting bays, and an expanded, state-of-the-art golf fitness area, the physical facilities now match the top-notch views and teachers.

One visit to Sea Island and you'll at least feel like a pro, if not play more like one.

ACKNOWLEDGEMENTS

THE IDEA FOR THIS BOOK CAME ABOUT when my long-time agent and good friend, Mac Barnhardt, received a call from Mike Beckerich, the publisher of Classics of Golf books. Mac and I had kicked around the prospect of a project like this for more than a decade, but it wasn't until Mike came along that it actually came to fruition. Like Mac and I, he truly believed in the value of a book of this type to help golfers of all levels experience a Tour-level training regimen. So a big thanks to Mike for making this finally happen, as well as my collaborators Rex Hoggard and Tom Cunneff, who helped to organize and corral all the routines and thoughts in my head and put them to paper. Thank you, as well, to Sea Island's staff photographer, Eliot VanOtteren, who was responsible for illustrating all the different routines in the book in such an artistic and informative manner.

From the time I was 10 years old, I knew I would be involved in physical fitness in some way. I grew up in a small central Pennsylvania town where my parents taught me about work ethic and a daily commitment to doing my best, so I really want to say to my mom, Karen, and my dad, Ben, how much I appreciate all you've done for me.

At the start of my career at PGA National in Palm Beach Gardens, Fla., I was able to work with two great visionary instructors, Mike Adams and Dr. Gary Wiren, who were among the first to connect the dots between function and form. Thank you both for your trust and insights. There were lots of other teaching pros—too many to mention by name—that I worked with along the way who bought into the importance of a golf fitness program. I couldn't have gotten to where I am without their support.

More recently, I've been fortunate to represent one of the finest golf resorts in the world, Sea Island Resort, which boasts perhaps the best and most scenic teaching facility anywhere. I can't thank the past and present leadership at Sea Island enough for their vision to assemble the best teaching team in the business, including Jack Lumpkin, Gale Peterson, Todd Anderson, Craig Allen, Mike Shannon, Jared Zak, and Dr. Morris Pickens. Every day I feel like I'm in the lineup for the 1927 Yankees.

Two other instructors I'd be remiss in not singling out are Butch Harmon and Mike Bender. Along with Todd, they collectively validated how important physical fitness is to the best players in the game. Thank you for your friendship and all you've done for me.

Finally, I need to express to my wife, Pam, and my children, Madison, Jacob, and Colton, how much you mean to me and how much I appreciate all the support you've given to me. It's been your love and inspiration that provided the peace of mind I needed to succeed.

See, it all comes back to balance and symmetry—and having a good team behind you!

—*Randy Myers*